the Marmaduke TREASURY
to
Helen and Richard
MORIN
With Best Wishes!
from Brad Anderson
and
MARMADUKE!

Books in the Sheed Andrews and McMeel Treasury Series

The Family Circus Treasury by Bil Keane

The Ziggy Treasury by Tom Wilson

The Momma Treasury by Mell Lazarus

The Marmaduke Treasury by Brad Anderson

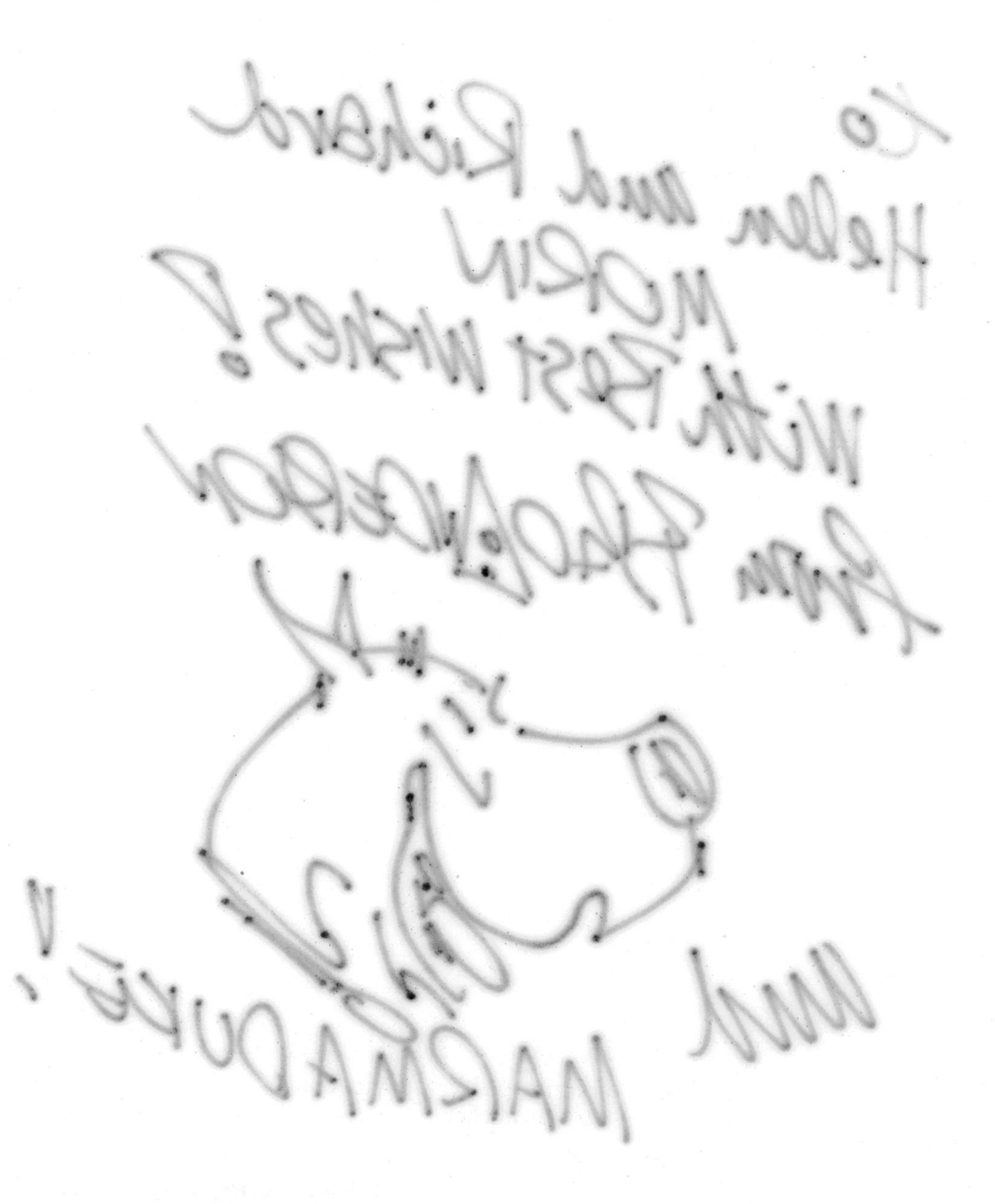

by Brad Anderson

Foreword by Charles M. Schulz

Sheed Andrews and McMeel, Inc.
Subsidiary of Universal Press Syndicate
Kansas City

 For information write Sheed Andrews and McMeel, Inc., Subsidiary of Universal Press Syndicate, 6700 Squibb Road, Mission, Kansas 66202.

ISBN: 0-8362-1108-1 cloth
0-8362-1107-3 paper
Library of Congress Catalog Card Number: 78-54706

To my wife, Barbara, and my children . . .
Christine, Craig, Paul and Mark, who shared
this "Dog's Life" with me.

Foreword

The quality I like best about "Marmaduke" as a newspaper feature is that it is fun to look at. The older I get, the more critical I become of the work I see being done by my contemporaries. When I evaluate a comic feature, I look for a pleasant appearance. It follows, then, that the right combination of drawing and writing will result in its being either funny or, in the case of an adventure strip, exciting. Good characters and good personalities are also an absolute must, and I think Marmaduke is a perfect lead character. Few cartoonists have been able to caricature a dog as well as Brad Anderson with his huge, ungainly, and lovable creature.

I think I might like to own a dog like Marmaduke, for I like dogs you can talk to. I don't especially like being destroyed by exuberance and clumsiness, of course, but I could tolerate that as long as a few laughs were included. Marmaduke would be handy as a watchdog in these perilous times, too, for if an intruder came into my house, I could always throw Marmaduke at him (if I could lift him). If the intruder were climbing the bedroom stairs, I would roll Marmaduke down the stairs and bowl the villain over.

At any rate, I am grateful for this collection of "Marmaduke" cartoons. I like good memories.

Charles M. Schulz

Number One Snoopy Place
February 7, 1978

Someone once asked me, "How do you come up with those funny situations every day?" The answer is . . . I think like a dog!

Marmaduke didn't begin life as a puppy but materialized in 1954 as a fully grown cartoon dog in Jamestown, New York. He was modeled after a boxer named Bruno. As can be seen in the accompanying photos, Bruno was something of a character, a clown, and a complete exhibitionist. He was also lovable, loyal, and fearless. That last attribute finally got him into trouble.

Bruno was owned by Dick Mabee, my stepdad's son, and he lived with Mom and Dad while Dick was in the Air Force. Dick was Bruno's master, or at least he thought he was, because Bruno thought of Dick as *his* pet! Actually he thought all people were his pets and he loved dragging his two-legged friends for fast runs around the block. One day he slipped his chain and, according to witnesses, met an untimely end while trying to face down an onrushing locomotive, barking defiantly at the monster as it bore down on him. I'm sure Bruno thought it would turn and run.

My interest in cartooning dates back to early childhood. My favorite subjects in school were drawing, baseball, and playground.

One winter, when I was very young and long before television, I suffered an extended illness. To amuse myself, I filled my tablets with drawings of the comic characters appearing in daily newspapers. From then on, my homework papers were adorned with "Popeye," "Mickey Mouse," "Krazy Kat," and all the other wonderful characters appearing on the comic pages.

Eventually, I began to develop my own comic characters and used them to decorate my homework and test papers. My geometry teacher accumulated the largest collection of cartoons and was still smiling when my grades slipped from C to D.

My career as a "professional" cartoonist began when I sold my first cartoons to an aviation magazine while still in high school. After graduation I joined the U.S. Navy, taking with me to boot camp a budding career and a box full of pens, ink, and paper. Looking back, I wonder how I ever got my little portable studio past some of those white glove inspections . . . but I did! It even went with me aboard ship and on sea duty in the Pacific during World War II.

WHAT MAKES YOU THINK I'VE GONE HOLLYWOOD?

After a few years, I had to make a choice between being a diesel engineman in the Navy or a career as a full-time cartoonist. Being a cartoonist sounded like more fun. So I married my high school sweetheart, Barbara Jones, took my discharge and Veteran's Bill to Syracuse University, and enrolled in the School of Fine Arts.

After four years I graduated and discovered that I was still a cartoonist. By this time, I was selling to the *Saturday Evening Post, Collier's,* and many other magazines. I also discovered that I was a father when Barb introduced me to my daughter, Christine. Later on, we added three sons: Craig, Paul, and Mark.

Of course, pets have always been a big part of our family. In fact, at times I thought we had our own zoo. The children would bring home "lost" cats, dogs, chickens, ducks, fish, and anything else that could walk, crawl, slither, or swim. Along with my family and pets, my cartoon career continued to grow.

About this time I was selling some funny dog cartoons to a farm magazine and was falling down laughing at the hilarious antics of Bruno, when I received a letter from Phil Leeming, a gagwriter, suggesting that we try and collaborate on a dog cartoon for newspaper syndication. All the right elements were there and it took only a short time to put everything together and create the right character.

Many names were kicked back and forth, but "Marmaduke" finally stuck. I drew up a month of cartoons and shipped them off to National Newspaper Syndicate in Chicago. The rest is history.

Unfortunately, Phil passed away a few years later. His wife, Dorothy, wrote gags for a while, but soon the gags as well as the art became my responsibility.

In 1960, we moved to Vista, California, a rural area where our little zoo overflowed until the children grew up and began leaving home. Last year Barb and I moved into a townhouse in Yuma, Arizona, along with our little Chihuahua-terrier, Dazy.

The first question most people ask me is, do I own a Great Dane? I hate to disappoint people but the answer is no, I have never owned a Great Dane. Marmaduke was really an exaggeration of Bruno, the boxer, but I felt that a large dog would make a much funnier cartoon character. So Marmaduke grew, and grew, and . . . .

"He wants you to buy HIM."

"Look! He brought home another **souvenir!**"

"Good gravey! What's he done now?"

"Mrs. Frawley was going to keep me after school, but Marmaduke came in and got me!"

"Oh! Oh! He's had another run-in with the dog-catcher!"

"I believe he wants to take you for a walk."

"Hey! Where did Marmaduke go?"

"He's out in the yard. I tied him to the fence."

"I guess he IS spoiled a little . . . but then, he's an only dog."

"Their baby said his first word today . . . Marmaduke."

"Wasn't it nice of Marmaduke to meet you at the bus stop with your umbrella?"

"Gosh, Marmaduke! Can't I even LOOK?"

"Okay! Okay! I know dinner is ready!"

"How many times do I have to tell you? I haven't GOT any mail for the Winslows today!"

"Well, maybe you can ride in the front seat with Daddy NEXT time, honey."

"He oughta teach that dog to heel."

"Doggone it! Does he always have to be so glad to see us?"

"Oh, oh! That's his favorite chair!"

"Chocolate malted . . . coke . . . root beer . . . and a T-bone steak, well-done."

"You forgot to kiss me goodbye!"

"What's the charge?"

"I can hear it!
I can *hear* it!"

"Now don't try to tell me that *dog* was traveling down the highway at 65 miles per hour!"

"You'll have to take it over to him, dear. You know he likes to have his breakfast in bed."

"You're not even a legitimate exemption . . . you're just dead loss!"

"Well, I don't like to look at your face across the breakfast table every morning either!"

"No nothing's wrong. He just got tired of walking."

"Phil made him another new dog house, but Marmaduke huffed, and he puffed . . . "

"I don't *want* to go for a walk!"

"He gets a big kick out of my trying to teach him tricks . . . Just lies there and laughs at me."

"Say! Do you know he did that last hundred yards in nine and two fifths seconds?"

"Phil, I think Marmaduke wants to come in."

"You'll just have to leave that spot uncut. That's where he's studying a colony of ants!"

"No! Marmaduke can't come out and raid garbage pails tonight!"

"What happened to the Snyders? They said they'd be here at eight sharp!"

"Marmaduke wants to see you about that mousetrap you set under the kitchen table."

"What the heck — let's leave him outside tonight!"

"Don't get any ideas. This is *my* roast beef!"

"Er — Howdy, folks . . . just passing through . . ."

"Oh — this is *good*! Marmaduke is going to give his imitation of Phil!"

"Look, Fred! There goes Marmaduke taking his pet man for a walk!"

"I'm counting how many bites he takes . . . One dollar, two dollars, three . . ."

"Watch me make him sit down. Stand up, Marmaduke! . . . Stand up, boy!"

"Doesn't that feel good? Take the brush inside and show it to the folks."

"Who's your little helper, Winslow?"

"He not only chases cars, he *catches* them!"

"Madam, he'll just *have* to make up his mind! He's tried on every coat in the place!"

"He saw his reflection in the window."

"Police? I want to report a peeping dog!"

"We hardly see him anymore since Snyder got that new car."

"That's all now . . . no more hitchikers!"

"You keep Marmaduke away from my Billy! I asked him what he wanted to be when he grew up — and he said a *DOG*!"

"That'll be $2.15"

"He must be catching cold. Didja hear that sneeze?"

"He started to grow on us . . . then he grew — and grew — and grew!!!!"

"Your husband's made a friend!"

"Find anything interesting?"

"Your Daddy's going to ask for a raise."

"Mornin', Marmaduke! How's the appetite?"

"Phil! — and you, too, Marmaduke!"

" 'Bout time you two came dragging in!"

"Dottie! Did you hear a noise downstairs?"

"I don't know. Burying a bone, or digging a basement, I guess!"

"— then I add the whites of three eggs, and —'

"What could he be trying to tell you?"

"Mr. Winslow! Come over here and stop this serenade!"

"— a little overweight. I'm putting him on a high protein diet of steak, rib roasts, calves liver —"

"What do you want . . . a push?"

"I told you yesterday not to give that *big* dog a bone!"

"Can't you two be friends?"

"Steady, Boy!"

"That's one of life's greatest rewards, . . . the love of a dog!"

"Oh, him! Mother told him to keep an eye on me"

". . . and if you want to raise a window you just push a button."

"... and as I gaze into your intelligent faces..."

"C'mon, Stonewall, it's time to go home!"

"Throw it anywhere. Marmaduke'll carry it over to the Winslows'."

"If you wanna help, get a towel!"

"Try to pretend it's not there!"

"Okay, now gimme the wrench . . . ."

"Under 'Purpose of Loan', he wrote *Dog Food*!"

"That one?"

" . . . and don't *ever* speak to me in that tone again, Phil Winslow!"

"I wasn't whistling at *you*, stupid!"

"I see you have a dog."

"He's baby sitting while the mother looks for worms!"

"Aha!"

"Well! You never hold *ME* on your lap!"

"I hope he's enjoying the view!"

"I'd swear I just heard the noon whistle!"

"This is NOT the time to play fetch!"

"Yoo hoo! Anybody ho . . . . ."

"He likes to stick his head out of the window."

"No, Dottie and I NEVER argue about who is boss!"

"I can lick any . . . er . . . human being in the house!"

"It's just coincidence, silly!"

"Daddy and I didn't catch a thing!"

"She'll be right down!"

"Let's give him a B-A-T-H!"

"At times, Phil acts almost canine!"

"I've been thinking very seriously of buying a Bengal tiger."

"Some guy down the street took the kids' baseball!"

"Right here — where it says 'Master' — why did you write 'None'?"

"There! THAT fence ought to keep him in his own yard!"

"Am I glad to see YOU!"

"I'D never have the nerve to do that!"

"How about something to slow him down?"

"You'll like the roomy back seat!"

"I thought your name began with a 'W', Winslow!"

"So THAT'S where my money goes!"

"Sure I'll lend you five bucks, Fred . . . . as soon as Marmaduke gets your scent!"

"What size were they?"

"How long is he in for?"

"Guess who!"

"He's trying to tell us something, I'm afraid."

"That's MARMADUKE'S chair!"

"He's STARING at me!"

"Of course you may go bowling tonight! Go ahead and go!"

"We DID send him to obedience school! He was expelled!"

"What're we supposed to do . . . . . DANCE home?"

"He found a wallet! Maybe there's a reward!"

"No, he doesn't eat between meals. With HIM, there ARE no between-meals!"

"He was chasing his tail and CAUGHT it!"

"Is that the ONLY piece he knows?"

"See what I mean about waiting for the light?"

"I don't WANT to play 'fetch'!"

". . . Six . . . seven . . . eight . . . nine . . . TEN!" ". . . Er . . . eleven . . . twelve . . . thirteen . . ."

"PLEASE stop saving my life!"

"Let him stay there as long as he wants! We're getting paid by the hour!"

"He's got the first-day-of-school blues!"

"They followed Marmaduke home. Can he KEEP them?"

"Get away from that refrigerator!"

"Imagine bein' locked outta your OWN home!"

"You know that door you sold me that opens at the sound of my horn? Well . . . ."

"As long as we're new in the neighborhood, maybe you'd better double-lock the front door!"

"Wait, dear, don't hang up! Marmaduke wants to say 'Woof - woof' to you!"

"I know you brought cake flour home yesterday, dear, but now I need 10 pounds more!"

"You're not kidding anybody!"

"He's here again, John — that nice dog that keeps bill collectors away!"

"Awfully dull day! I'd like to see something exciting happen."

"My, what a dweat big, adorable doggie-woggie!"

"Ever notice how this car seems to lean to one side?"

MARMADUKE
by BRAD ANDERSON
KEE RAK
KRASH
KRAK
KABOOM
RUMBLLLLLLL
BAROOOMM
KA
RAK
OH-OH!
RUMBLE
GUESS WHO
IT'S OUR FOUL WEATHER FRIEND
Sigh
AH-HUH
DOGGONE FUNNY
HE GETS A BIG BANG OUT OF THIS!
CHOMP
CHOMP
WHEN WE LIGHT FIRECRACKERS OUR DOG TAKES THEM IN HIS MOUTH AND PUTS THEM OUT! (THEN HE EATS THEM)
SRS: DORIS PELTIER DANBURY, TEXAS
Ⓟ, © 1972 NAT'L. News. Syn.
BRAD ANDERSON

LOOK PHIL! HE'S DREAMING AGAIN!
HE LOOKS SO FUNNY WHEN HE'S DREAMING!
YEH! HE KILLS ME!
LOOK! HE'S WALKING IN HIS SLEEP!
THIS IS TOO MUCH!
IT'S A RIOT!
WHAT'S HE DOING?
HE OPENED THE REFRIG AND ATE OUR ROAST!
THAT WASN'T FUNNY!
ZZZZZZZ
Ⓗ, © 1973 NAT'L. News. Syn.
BRAD ANDERSON

Marmaduke
by Brad Anderson
WHAT CAN WE DO?
LET'S PLAY HOUSE!
WITH OUR DOLLS!
I WISH WE HAD A REAL BABY DOLL
I'M GETTIN' OUTA HERE!
WE CAN DRESS UP MARMADUKE!
JUST LIKE A REAL BABY!
© 1978 United Feature Syndicate, Inc.
AN' WE CAN TAKE HIM FOR A RIDE!
IT'S TIME FOR HIS BOTTLE!
LOOK AT THE BIG BABY
HAR!
HAR!
HAR!
HAR!
HA
HE...
AHHH...
HE WANTS YOU TO PLAY WITH US!
LUTHER! WHAT ARE YOU DOING?
WE'RE PLAYING HOUSE
AND I'M HIS GRAMPAW!
BRAD ANDERSON

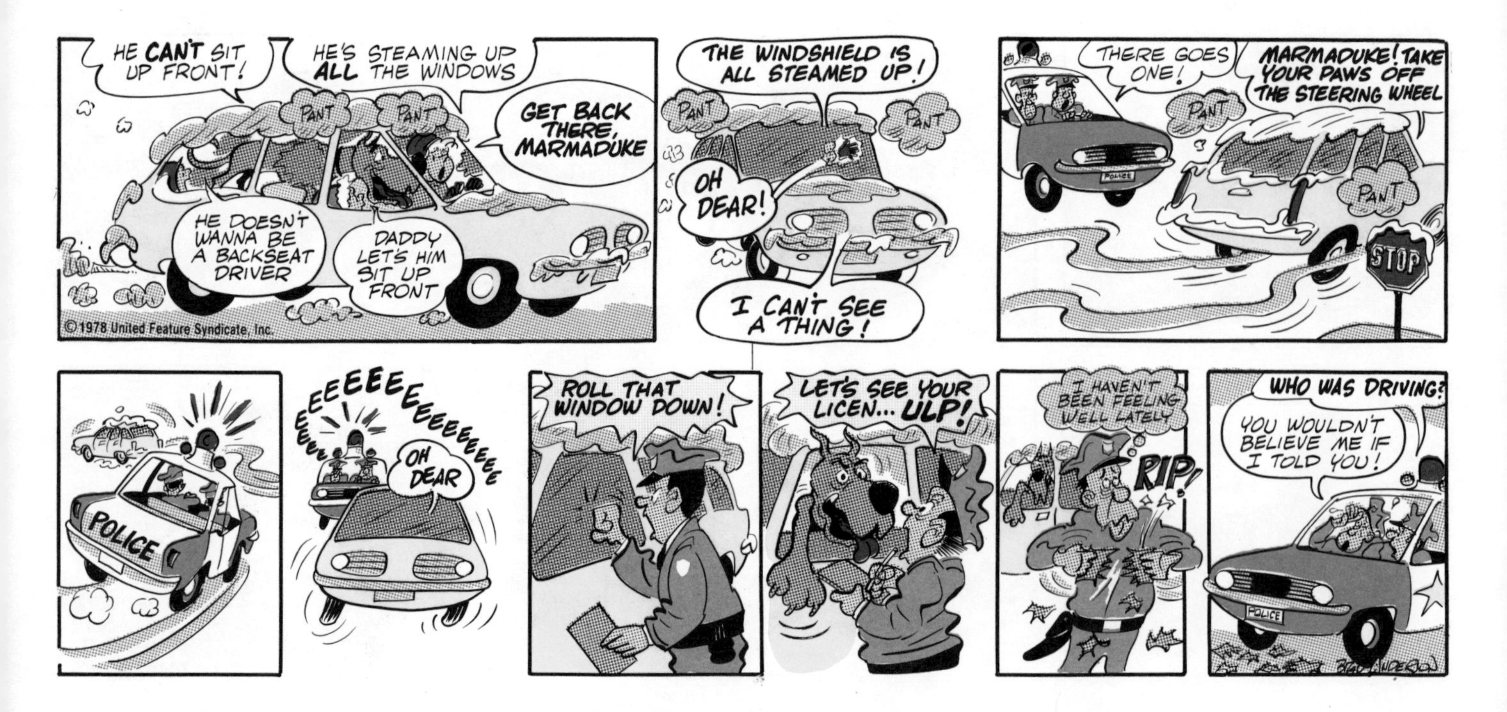
HE CAN'T SIT UP FRONT!
HE'S STEAMING UP ALL THE WINDOWS
PANT
PANT
GET BACK THERE, MARMADUKE
HE DOESN'T WANNA BE A BACKSEAT DRIVER
DADDY LET'S HIM SIT UP FRONT
© 1978 United Feature Syndicate, Inc.
THE WINDSHIELD IS ALL STEAMED UP!
PANT
PANT
OH DEAR!
I CAN'T SEE A THING!
THERE GOES ONE!
MARMADUKE! TAKE YOUR PAWS OFF THE STEERING WHEEL
PANT
PANT
STOP
POLICE
EEEEEEEEEEEEEEEEE
OH DEAR
ROLL THAT WINDOW DOWN!
LET'S SEE YOUR LICEN... ULP!
I HAVEN'T BEEN FEELING WELL LATELY
RIP!
WHO WAS DRIVING?
YOU WOULDN'T BELIEVE ME IF I TOLD YOU!
POLICE
BRAD ANDERSON

MARMADUKE
by BRAD ANDERSON
HAVE A NICE DAY!
BYE MOM
IS MARMADUKE GOING TO SCHOOL WITH US?
DOGS DON'T GO TO SCHOOL
DOGS STAY ON VACATION ALL YEAR LONG
THEY ARE LUCKY
I WISH I WAS A DOG!
I HEAR THE SCHOOL BUS COMING!
OH! I FORGOT MY LUNCH!
THANKS MARMADUKE!
HERE'S THE BUS!
ALL ABOARD
PANT
WAIT FOR ME!
OOF!
HURRY UP LISA!
STOP FOR SCHOOL BUS
VISTA SCHOOL
YOU'LL BE LATE!
® © 1972 NAT'L. News. Syn.
WAIT FOR LISA
VOOM
STOP FOR SCHOOL BUS
HOORAY FOR MARMADUKE
BRAD ANDERSON

HURRY UP AND BRING THE EGGS
I MADE A BLUE EASTER EGG!
LOOK AT THIS RED ONE!
HEY MARMADUKE
GET YOUR NOSE OUT OF OUR EGGS
WE DON'T NEED YOUR HELP!
GET OUTA HERE
MOVE
MARMADUKE! DON'T WAG YOUR TAIL!
OH
NO
® © 1973 NAT'L. News. Syn.
BRAD ANDERSON
HE SORTA LOOKS LIKE AN EASTER EGG
I'D SAY HE LOOKS MORE LIKE A BAD EGG!

MARMADUKE
by BRAD ANDERSON
WHAT A BEAUTIFUL DAY!
I LOVE OCTOBER AN ALL THE PRETTY LEAVES!
YEH! AN THE DUMP IS REALLY PRETTY TOO!
TRASH
DUKE'S TRASH SERVICE
HERE WE ARE, ON MARMADUKE'S STREET!
I HATE TO THINK ABOUT IT!
REMEMBER THE LAST TIME?
HE INSPECTED THE WHOLE LOAD
IT TOOK TWO HOURS
WE GOTTA BE MORE SMART THIS TIME
OUT THINKING MARMADUKE AINT EASY
I GOT THIS FANTASTIC PLAN
I BET ROBBING A BANK IS EASIER!
THAT'S HOW I GOT THE PLAN!
FROM WATCHING THE LATE MOVIE ON T-V
I CUT THE ENGINE AN' ROLL SILENTLY TO THE CURB
YOU RACE AROUND THE BACK OF THE HOUSE AN DIVERT MARMADUKE'S ATTENTION
I GRAB THE CAN
AN' DASH FOR THE TRUCK!
OOPS
WHAT WENT WRONG?
IT'S EASIER TO ROB BANKS!!
© 1972 NAT'L. News. Syn.
10-1
BRAD ANDERSON

PHONE
SHRIEK! YIP YIP (HELP)
GRRR
Z
DUPER DOG
© 1973 NAT'L. News. Syn.
YIP YIP
ARF
OOF
LOOK AT THAT SILLY EXPRESSION! DO YOU SUPPOSE HE'S DREAMING?
NO... PROBABLY HAVING GAS PAINS!
BRAD ANDERSON

AARROOOOOOO WOOOORRRRAAOO
MARMADUKE
by BRAD ANDERSON
GOODNESS!
WELL! WOULD YOU LOOK AT THAT!
ARUF RUFF RAFF AROOOOOO WOOF WUF
ROOO ROO WOOF!
WHAT WAS THAT ALL ABOUT?
I DON'T KNOW...
I MISSED THE PUNCH LINE
DOG GONE FUNNY
THAT MEANS I WIN THE FIGHT!
GRRRRR
When anybody FIGHTS or ARGUES in the family... Our MINIATURE PINSCHER breaks it up by GROWLING!
KATHY HANSON JAMESTOWN, N.Y.
BRAD ANDERSON
© 1972 NAT'L. News. Syn.

GOOD HEAVENS!
WHERE IS HE GOING?
MR SNYDER JUST FILLED HIS SWIMMING POOL
I DIDN'T KNOW MR SNYDER HAD A SWIMMING POOL
® © 1973 NAT'L. News. Syn.
OH SURE!
IT'S GREAT!
HE SAID ME AN MARMADUKE CAN SHARE IT WITH HIM...
IF WE DON'T TELL ANYONE!
BRAD ANDERSON

MARMADUKE
by BRAD ANDERSON
I'M LEARNING A LOT OF NEW WORDS TODAY!
IN STEREO!
DID YOU HEAR THE NEWS?
SOMEONE TIPPED OVER MR SNYDERS GARBAGE CAN!
AN SOMEBODY DUG UP MRS ROWE'S PETUNIAS
AN SOMEBODY RIPPED MRS WILLIAM'S CLOTHES OFF THE LINE!
AN SOMEBODY GOT MUD ON MR MCFADDEN'S NEW CAR!
THERE MUST BE A DEVIL RUNNING LOOSE IN OUR NEIGHBORHOOD
BUT WHO?
WHAT'S YOUR MOM DOING?
I GUESS SHE'S MAKING A SIGN!
TO WHOM IT MAY CONCERN: MARMADUKE HAS BEEN LOCKED IN THE BACK YARD ALL DAY!!
®, © 1972 NAT'L News. Syn.
BRAD ANDERSON
DOG GONE FUNNY
AND DON'T FORGET TO WASH BEHIND YOUR EARS!
EVERY MORNING OUR BEAGLE RUFUS GOES IN THE BATHROOM ...FINDS A WET WASHCLOTH AND WASHES HIS FACE!
Se3: PAM GARDNER
EL CAJON, CA.

GRRRRRRRRRRUMBLE
GRRRRR
WHAT'S THE MATTER? DON'T YOU RECOGNIZE ME?
GRRR
IT'S ME... BARBARA!
?
®, © 1973 NAT'L. News. Syn.
ARRRRR
?
IT'S US!
HOW DO YOU LIKE OUR NEW OUTFITS?
CAN DOGS REALLY LAUGH?
BRAD ANDERSON
DOG GONE FUNNY
NO... SHE ISN'T SICK ... SHE'S A HYPOCHONDRIAC
Whenever we give OUR Dog, BOY, any MEDICINE ... OUR SHELTIE 'COOKIE' BEGS until we pretend to give her some
Kim HENRY, NEW BRITAIN CT.

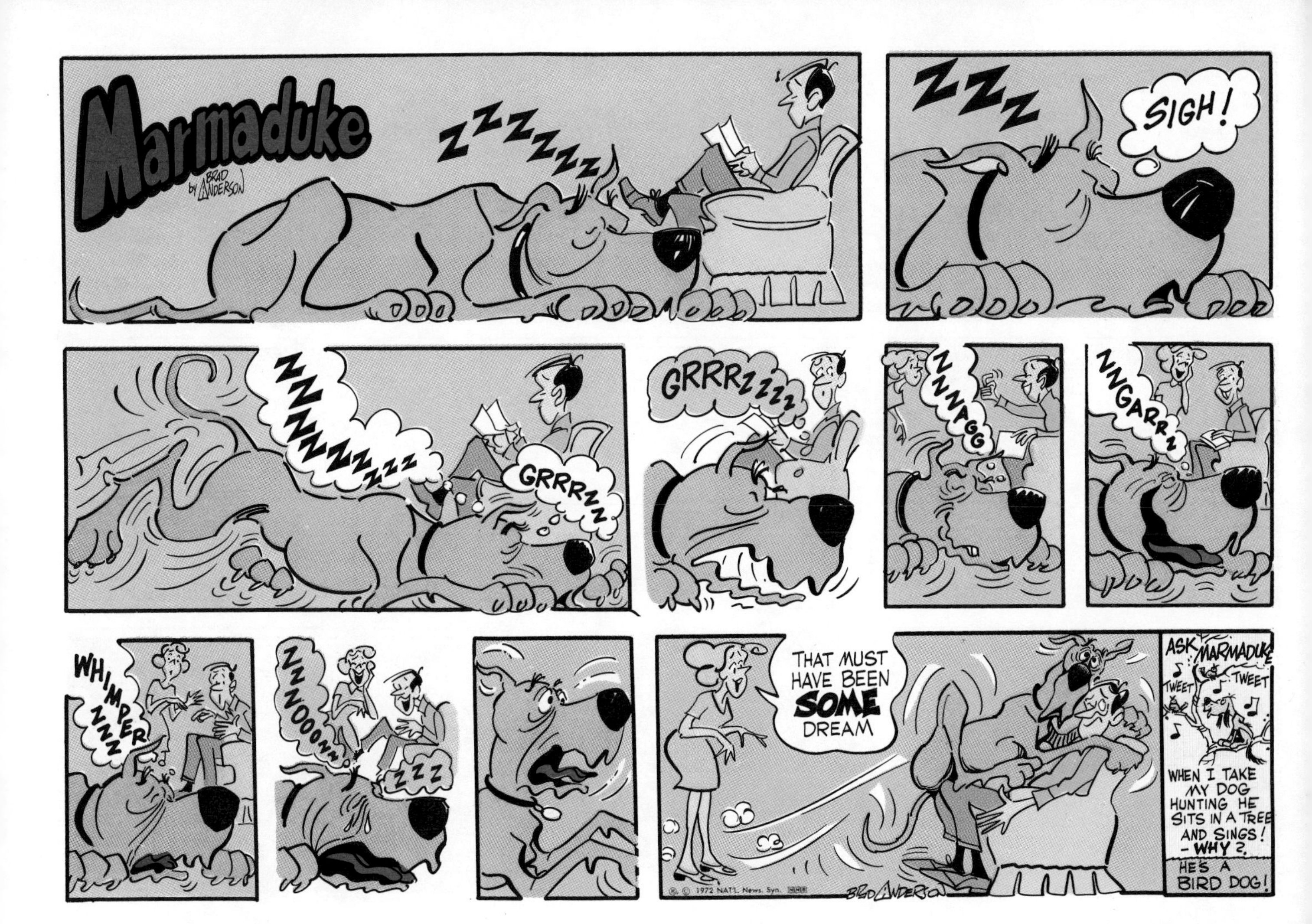
Marmaduke
by BRAD ANDERSON
ZZZZZZZ
ZZZ
SIGH!
NNNNZZZZZ
GRRRZZZ
GRRRZZZZ
ZZZZAGG
NNGARRZ
WHIMPER ZZZ
ZZZOOONN
ZZZ
THAT MUST HAVE BEEN SOME DREAM
ASK MARMADUKE
TWEET
TWEET
WHEN I TAKE MY DOG HUNTING HE SITS IN A TREE AND SINGS! - WHY ?
HE'S A BIRD DOG!
© 1972 NAT'L. News. Syn.
BRAD ANDERSON

?
© 1973 NAT'L. News. Syn.
MAR MA DUKE
COME BACK HERE...
WITH MY WIG!
BRAD ANDERSON

MARMADUKE
by BRAD ANDERSON
WOW! I WISH HE WUZ ON OUR FOOTBALL TEAM!
HEY! MARMADUKE IS LOOKING AT THE COMICS
CAN HE READ?
SURE! HE'S A SMART DOG!
NOW HE WANTS TO GO OUT
HE'S CLIMBING ON TOP OF HIS DOG HOUSE
MARMADUKE
JUST LIKE IN THE COMICS!
RIGHT ON!
® © 1972 NAT'L. News. Syn.
THUD
YOU GOTTA REMEMBER ONE THING MARMADUKE
YOU CAN'T BELIEVE EVERYTHING YOU SEE IN THE FUNNY PAPER!
BRAD ANDERSON
DOG GONE FUNNY
AW C'MON! LET US MAKE ONE FIRST DOWN!
NUTS
MY AIRDALE CROSS NAMED "BUD" AND OUR NEIGHBORS GERMAN SHEPHERD LOVE TO PLAY FOOTBALL AND THEY ARE A GREAT DEFENSE WHEN WE PLAY AGAINST THEM!
Sent: TOM INGALLS LOMA LINDA CA.

ZZZZZZZZZZ
WOOF WOOF
WOOF WOOF WOOF
WUF WUF
WOOF
® © 1973 NAT'L. News. Syn.
WOOF WOOF
WUF RUF
WOOF WOOF WOOF
IT'S ME... PHIL!
DON'T YOU RECOGNIZE ME...
IT'S JUST A NEW MUSTACHE!
YOU REALLY EMBARRASSED HIM!
BRAD ANDERSON

Marmaduke is master of the household, keeper of the peace in the neighborhood, protector of all the little animals, and one of the gang when playing with neighborhood children. Marmaduke dominates most situations. He's in charge and he knows it. But sometimes he ends up courting disaster, as shown on page 66.

The situations basically deal with real life. Sometimes when I draw a cartoon and think it might be too bizarre, fans of "Marmaduke" will write in and ask, "How did you ever guess what our dog did?"

Marmaduke can be happy, sad, sleepy, belligerent, pensive, contemplative, smug, laughable, superior, or even sophisticated. He can display almost any emotion, sometimes with just his eyes or a flick of the eyebrow.

Because Marmaduke was born in Jamestown, New York, I decided to make this western New York area his permanent home, thus enabling me to cover the full four seasons and come up with some fun-filled seasonal situations. And Marmaduke isn't the only character in the cartoon that was based upon a real character. Barbie was modeled by my daughter, Chris.

Little Billy, who first appeared as the neighbor's baby, was a composite of my three sons, who ranged from toddlers to preschool at the time. I even incorporated their speech patterns and "Marmaduke" became "Mommyduke." To avoid confusion, Billy eventually became a member of the Winslow family and mastered the pronunciation of "Marmaduke." In the strip, he began attending school a couple of years ago — not bad for a kid who is really over eighteen years old now!

Other cartoon characters, such as the garbage men and their truck, were modeled after a couple of real garbage men in Maple Springs, New York. Cave's Meat Market and the Whirl-Inn Hot Dog Drive-In are a couple of Marmaduke's favorite hangouts and they really exist. Door-to-door salesmen are really modeled after me when I was trying to work my way through college; and car salesmen always look like Carl Williams, a car-salesman-friend of mine. Photographers, postmen, dog catchers,

NEWS
jes
0-36

Jamestown Post-

JAMESTOWN, N.Y., TUESDAY, DECEMBER

Couple
jary
anel

Rendells,
ers Named
port Jan. 3

le man and his wife
g 48 county residents
rial jurors for the Jan-
of County Court, which
in Mayville. The cou-
ley and Doris Rendell,
nville.
ners drawn include:
Bargar, 304 Arlington
euben J. Carlson, 66
et; Virtue F. Chadwick,
Street; and Richard O.
nden Avenue.
e: Arthur H. Anderson,
amestown; Henry J. An-
ute 1, Fredonia; Arthur
asperger, 29, Norton
donia; Robert Bauer,
Sherman; Robert Carl
12 Pearl, Forestville;
Brown, Conewango Val-
an Brushaber, 65 Spring
donia; Norman Edgar
e 2, Frewsburg.
O. Button, Main Street,
C. Chauncey Clement,
Dewittville; Astor A.
Route 3, Forestville;
Damon, 30 North Alle-
gue, W.E.; Raymond E.
Route 1, Kennedy; Em-
ker, Route 2, Ashville;
Fisher, Box 522, Sinclair-
Diana Giddy, Route 1,

Gravink, East Main
ymer; Russell C. Hitch-
te 1, Falconer; Raymond
Dennison Road, Silver
rl H. Johnson, Route 1,
LaVerne C. Johnson,
Falconer; Herman W.
Route 1, Ashville; Car-
son, 215 Woodcrest
d; Homer C.

MARMADUKE AND CREATOR—Brad Anderson, Jamestown-born cartoonist who created the Marmaduke cartoon panel which starts in The Post-Journal next Monday, is shown at work at the drawing table in his home. Inset shows boxer dog owned by Dick Mabee of Jamestown, given credit for inspiring the Marmaduke series. —Post-Journal Staffoto

Judge Bodir
Presides at
Non-Jury Te

1 Man Sentenc
4 Plead Guilty,
Three Not-Gui

MAYVILLE — Cou
Hugh V. N. Bodine M
tenced one man, hear
guilty from four defe
pleas of innocence fron
ers at a non-jury term
Chester Teal, 28, Sper
Silver Creek, was sent
days in County Jail, bu
he had already be
while awaiting dispo
case. He was indicted
on a charge of crimin
ing a revolver, a mi
The defendant plea
the charge Monday
being sentenced. Acc
trict Attorney Edwin
the defendant was fo
bullets on his perso
fight and a gun, h
tained from anothe
found in his home
no permit for it. L
ams was his assign
Judge Bodine expr
that this would be
and others who may
without a license.
Among those plea
charges arising fr
handed up a wee
E. Spoon, Jr., 19
East, Pa., to gra
degree and a
attempted bur
The larceny i
a motor ve
Motors N
ed bur
ed

Dog Turns Doorknob, Brin

A clipping from a 1954 Jamestown **Post-Journal** *showing Brad drawing a Marmaduke cartoon along with an insert of Bruno . . . his model for Marmaduke.*

and other characters appearing in the feature are all caricatures of living people and friends (I hope). When names are needed in a caption or in a Sunday strip, such as found on page 54, I dig back into my past and use names of my former school chums. This is much easier than trying to make up names. They love it and it allows me to have Marmaduke living in a neighborhood of people I really know. Incidentally, Mr. Snyder has a real counterpart in Jamestown. Even their birthdays fall on the same day!

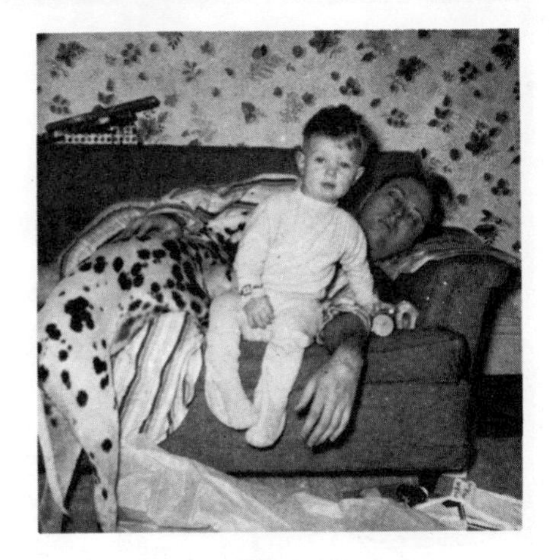

In 1954 Mark and Duchess help Brad dream up some Marmaduke cartoons.

My mother will appear from time to time — also aunts and uncles. And every construction worker is my cousin, Sol.

Any cat that appears is based upon our own Mama Kitty (page 98). She was really very sweet, but she did *not* like dogs, except those in our family. If a strange dog tried pushing our little Dazy around, Mama would go bouncing and hissing into the fray with fur standing on end, claws bared, and attack the intruder. Size never stopped her when a member of her family was in difficulty.

One night I was awakened by a terrible calamity on our patio. I dashed out of the house and found that Mama had cornered a poor old hound who unsuspectingly wandered in looking for a free meal. I grabbed Mama and the hound bounded out of the gate emitting the most distressing howls of fright. Our other dogs remained in their beds casually watching the whole show.

"Let me know how you like this new recipe!"

"You be the momma, you be the daddy and I'll be Marmaduke!"

"Isn't it wonderful, the way he plays with children?"

"Leave some for me!"

"Why, Madam, for a moment I thought you were Marilyn Mon - - - !"

"Chicken!"

"I'm getting sick and tired of looking at that same old face every day!"

"Hold it a minute, Mildred —"

"Say! That *is* good wax!"

"Any luck?"

"You're wasting your time, Snyder. He likes that stuff!"

"Wait a minute while I pull down the shade!"

"That's a good dog!"

"Where did you get *that?*"

"Ketch it. Mommyduke — Ketch!"

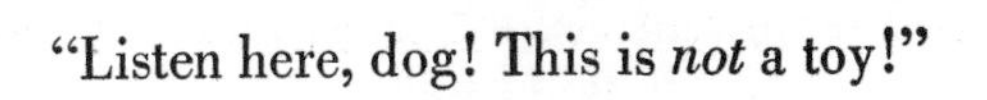

"Listen here, dog! This is *not* a toy!"

"Thtick 'em up, thtranger!"

"Officer, arrest that masher!"

"Well, Dottie went visiting today and there was no one to mind him, so . . ."

"Great dog you have, Winslow! I've been trying to break up that water cooler gang for years!"

"... er ... thanks for waiting!"

"Hey! How about *this* one?"

"They haven't lost a ball game all season."

"Come down, Marmaduke! The man wants to take his train away now!"

"You have it backwards, Miss. It's Dreamboat who's keeping *Marmaduke* out late!"

It'th no uthe, Mommyduke...she knowth you're here!

"If animals could vote, he'd be our next president!"

"If she gives you a hard time, call Marmaduke!
HE'LL know what to do!"

"Pictures of the dog show winners!"

"Aren't we OVERDOING it a bit, pal?"

"You're a gwown-up . . . tie it!"

I don't WANT to cross the street! I was just waiting for some old lady to come along!

Now I won't have to jump up every five minutes to open the door for him!

"Mmmmm! Now a little more to the left!"

"Nice catch!"

When he wants to lie down, why can't he just flop?

Why the sudden mania for walking in the rain?!?

Well, there's 'Old Faithful'!

It says "All MEN are created equal"... it doesn't say a thing about DOGS!!

...Dinner is ready.

Smart dog!

Now, if we could only figure out some place for you to go!

Look! Mommyduke hath a car of hith own to play wif!

There goes the Pied Piper of Maple Street!

Hear that siren? They're coming for you!

You're not like those uppity uptown dogs... you're real people!

Winslow thinks the world of that dog!

He's upset. He tried to chase away the rain, and it wouldn't go.

Well, at least Winslow isn't being dragged around at the end of a leash anymore!

Here he comes again...with the wretched, the homeless, the hungry...

First time on the ice?

He wants a bagful of bread crumbs for his friends.

Oh, I forgot to bring his transistor radio and lemon drops.

Sure he's a smart dog! Ask him something!

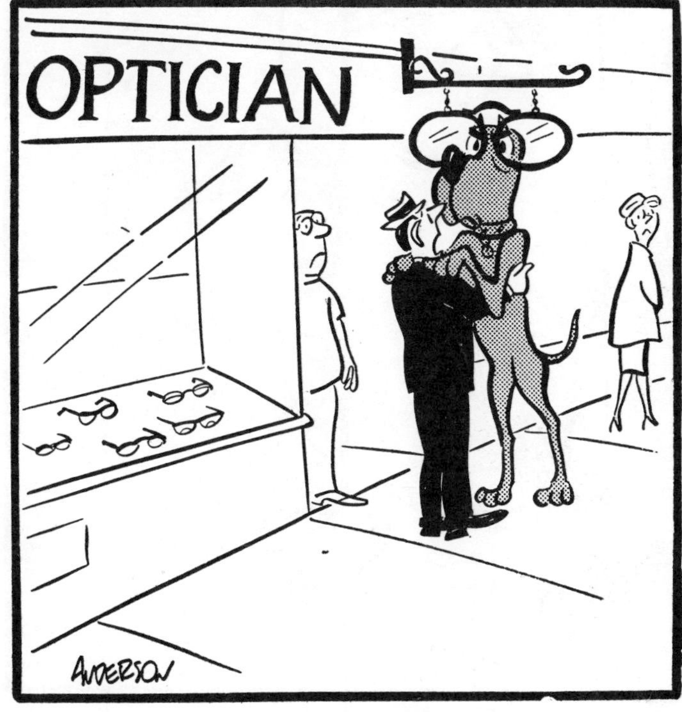

Satisfied?

There they go...turning him loose on the unsuspecting world again!

Kin Mithter Thnyder come out an' play wif uth?

We picked some flowers for you, Mommy!

Marmaduke's not in. Whom shall I say called?

Celebrating something?

Can't you find some other place to entertain your guests?

"But can you support her in the style to which she's accustomed?"

Cut it out! You know it's me!

"No, don't tell me! Let me guess! Is it Lassie?...Rin Tin Tin?..."

Where did you get the fancy waiter, Mr. Winslow?

"It's bad enough to have to buy it...
let alone feed it to him!"

"He's our mascot, water boy and substitute right tackle!"

"Come on out. You're supposed to be our mascot -- rain OR shine!"

"Daddy, Marmaduke doesn't think your new suit fits!"

"He's easy to cook for...He doesn't care if it's porterhouse, T-bone, sirloin, filet mignon..."

"Me an' Mommyduke have been kicked out of better places than this!"

"If you're so tired, take a nap!"

"It doesn't do a thing for you!"

"Thanks, Marmaduke."

"I don't care how you serve the eggs...Just serve them!"

"Who said chivalry is dead?"

"I bet HE'LL be glad when school starts!"

"The mailman growled back at him!"

"Good boy! Good boy!"

"Man! Talk about an honest dog!"

"You're RIGHT, Mommie! It IS more fun when you make a game of it!"

"Okay, okay, you've made your point! We'll get you a new one!"

"Well, you must have done SOMETHING that annoyed him!"

"Your seams are crooked!"

"You look scared, Marmaduke! We better go inside!"

"I think he wants you to take him for a spin around the block!"

"It's your favorite dish . . . FOOD!"

"He's even getting to LOOK like a hamburger!"

"He's WOMAN'S best friend, too!"

"NO, THANKS !!"

"Look! HE'S learned to buy on credit, too!"

"I had no choice . . . He keeps having guests!"

"Every time Marmaduke tries to bark,
the bird says, 'Shut up'!"

"Can my friend enter your contest?"

"Your dog stole my arrows!"

"The best way to raise a dog like this?
How about a block and tackle?"

"Just one more bedtime story, then you'll have to go to sleep!"

"It's a matter of pride! He just won't chase amateurs!"

"I gotta be careful! It mighta been Marmaduke!"

"Oh, we should reward them
for being such angels!"

"Mumps or just a mouth full of food?!?"

"Marmaduke! Elephants don't chase cars!"

"Now watch his eyes light up when his blanket comes by!"

"How would YOU like to stay home all day with no one but HIM to talk to?"

". . . Furthermore, do you promise to love, honor and . . ."

"Make your pitch fast . . . He's sizing you up!"

"They can't fool me. It's two dogs."

"Guess where we dug a hole today!"

"He just came in and we're defrosting him!"

"Hey, Pop, Marmaduke's as long as he is high! Then how come he isn't square?!"

"This ought to keep him from barking for a while . . . I'm feeding him peanut butter!"

"Mr. Winslow, I want to thank you for helping put my boy through college!"

"Guess what, Phil! The kids taught Marmaduke a new trick today!"

"Marmaduke plays right, center and left field . . . all at once!"

"Now, let's see, Mr. Winslow . . . You have a wife, a son, a daughter, and whatever THAT is!"

"Marmaduke, are you MY pet or am I YOURS?"

"It's his hubcap collection! You think he chases cars just for exercise?!"

"Thank heaven, the cavalry has FINALLY arrived!!"

"You bad, bad dog! NOW I'll have to put in a little overtime at $7.50 an hour!"

"Great help, isn't he, Snyder? I bet you've never mowed your lawn THAT fast before!"

"Well, what followed you home today?"

"Now, once you get past our 'official greeter,' your day is made!"

"Sorry, Marmaduke, recess isn't for an hour yet."

"I will NOT sing 'Happy Birthday' to Marmaduke or any OTHER dog!"

"OUT!!!"

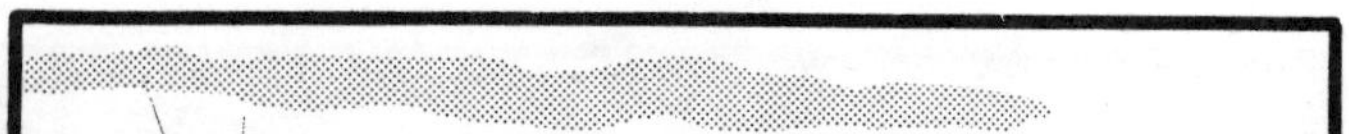

"By the way, I finally taught Marmaduke to bring me the paper every morning!"

"The game's off! He doesn't want to be the last of the Mohicans!"

"Yes, he's a great watch dog . . . He watches me buy the meat, he watches Dottie cook it, he . . . "

"Why, yes, we have 'something extra dirty' you can clean as a demonstration!"

"He's strictly non-partisan! He snarled through the Democratic convention and growled through the GOP convention!"

"Somebody to see you!"

"Knock it off, Marmaduke! I didn't come within 50 feet of you!"

"Why can't you learn to hibernate all winter?!"

"Bar none, this is the most embarrassing moment of my life!"

"Thanks to that dog, twice as many people come in to have their eyes examined!"

"How do I know what it is? Maybe we dug up a prehistoric animal!"

"Is it a coincidence that, after he barked three times, you bid three spades?!"

"I'm getting philosophical about it. . . Maybe he'll discover oil someday!"

"NOW will you believe Phil wants you home?!"

"You heard what the Winslows said, Helen . . . IGNORE HIM!"

"Sorry, madam, but when he's heading home for dinner, NOTHING stops him!"

"But he wouldn't stop barking until I put in a dime!"

"I brought Tornado over so he could play with Marmaduke!"

"If there's going to be a reconciliation, one of you will have to swallow his pride!"

"C'mon, Nosey!"

I think you gave up smoking this afternoon.

We never should have told him we were on diets!

"Honestly, Mother! Phil wouldn't teach him to do a thing like THIS to you!"

"Wish I had a little helper like that on MY route!"

"Here! YOU throw it! I might miss Mr. Winslow!"

"He's helping until Santa Claus comes back from lunch!"

"An' a hundred pounds of steak for Marmaduke!"

...Not a creature was stirring, not even a....

"Marmaduke got a new collar, a new coat an' a new doghouse. Daddy got a new leash!"

Mrs. Winslow, we want to go home!

OOOOWWWARRRRROOOOOOOO
MARMADUKE
by BRAD ANDERSON
OWWWARRRRR
OOOOOOOOOOOOOOO
OOWWARROO
"YOU'RE HIS MASTER... IT'S UP TO YOU TO TELL HIM HE CAN'T SING IN THE CHILDREN'S CHOIR!"
"WHO ATE THE HEAD OFF MY CHOC'LAT BUNNY?"
®. © 1974 NAT'L. News. Syn.
MARMADUKE
by BRAD ANDERSON
BUT HE HAS TO COME! HE'S OUR LUCKY MASCOT!
6-8
®. © 1975 NAT'L. News. Syn.
WHY DOES THE SPORTS PAGE ALWAYS GET CHEWED UP? ISN'T THE REST OF THE PAPER TASTY?
FRANKLY, I THINK HE'S GETTING A LITTLE OVER-CONFIDENT!

MARMADUKE!
BY BRAD ANDERSON
YOU CAN'T FOOL ME. YOU ATE MY LOLLYPOP!
®, © 1976 NAT'L. News. Syn.
I DON'T WORRY ABOUT MUGGERS STEALING MY PURSE!
MARMADUKE
BY BRAD ANDERSON
10-13
"DID YOU HAVE TO BRING YOUR CAT TO SHOW-AND-TELL THE SAME DAY I BROUGHT MARMADUKE?"
"WHY CAN'T HE JUST STICK HIS HEAD OUT THE WINDOW?"
®, © 1974 NAT'L. News. Syn.
WHERE DID YOU LOSE PHIL?

MARMADUKE
by BRAD ANDERSON
TRICK OR TREAT, eh ? OKAY SHOW ME A TRICK !
®, © 1974 NAT'L. News. Syn.

MARMADUKE
by BRAD ANDERSON
®, © 1974 NAT'L. News. Syn.
"IT'S OKAY, MOM ! WE'RE PLAYING BEAUTY SHOP !"
"WHEN DID HE TAKE THIS SUDDEN INTEREST IN THE JOHNNY CARSON SHOW ?"
"YOUR HOSPITALITY OVERWHELMS ME !"

MARMADUKE
by BRAD ANDERSON
THIS IS YOUR LOCAL ZOO... FRAZZLED SPEAKING!
®, © 1974 NAT'L. News. Syn.
"WHOEVER HEARD OF A TERRARIUM MADE OF BONES?"
DOG GONE FUNNY
When we gave our COCKER-SPANIEL PUPPY her water she was very CONFUSED and ran and JUMPED INTO IT!
Sez LISA LOGAN WEST CHESTER, PA.
BUFFY

MARMADUKE
by BRAD ANDERSON
I GUESS I SHOULDN'T HAVE PAINTED YOUR TOENAILS!
®, © 1974 NAT'L. News. Syn.
I TOLD YOU MARMADUKE WAS HUMAN. HE EATS WEEDS JUST LIKE EUELL GIBBONS!

MARMADUKE
by BRAD ANDERSON
COOKIES
HEY GANG! MARMADUKE MADE IT THROUGH ENEMY LINES! HOT COCOA AND COOKIES!
®, © 1974 NAT'L. News. Syn.
I DONT THINK I COULD STAND IT WITH THE THERMOSTAT TURNED SO LOW... IF WE DIDN'T HAVE MARMADUKE

MARMADUKE
by BRAD ANDERSON
BRING FIVE HOT CHOCOLATES AND A BONE!
ATE ALL THE CANDY CANES OFF THE TREE!
®, © 1975 NAT'L. News. Syn.
CAN YOU SEE THE PIECES TO MY PUZZLE?

MARMADUKE
by BRAD ANDERSON
Hospital
FIRSt AID
LITTLE NURSE
"NOT ME! I'M NOT GONNA PRACTICE MOUTH-TO-MOUTH 'SUSITATION!"
®, © 1974 NAT'L. News. Syn.
SLURP!
"I'LL LICK MY OWN CHOPS IF YOU DON'T MIND!"
DOG GONE FUNNY
When my Poodle decides she wants to go walking she takes her leash in her mouth and GOES!
Sez: Randy Lee HOUSTON, Tex.
MARMADUKE
by BRAD ANDERSON
® © 1975 NAT'L. News. Syn.
EVERYTIME MARMADUKE VISITS THE VET WE GET A GRAND SEND-OFF FROM ALL THE WELL-WISHERS!
HE'S AT THE INQUISITIVE STAGE!
How many times I gotta tell you... DON'T WAG YOUR TAIL!
DOG GONE FUNNY
Our BLACK LAB 'JIM' has a tail like a sledgehammer!
FROM JOE CURREN, BELLEVIEW, WASH.

OOL BUS
MARMADUKE GOT IN THE CATNIP AGAIN!
DOG GONE FUNNY
ARE YOU STILL MAD?
AMBER THORP Sez..
When our cockapoo had her hair cut and styled SHE wouldn't let us touch her. SHE Just sat in a corner and gave us DIRTY LOOKS for a WEEK!
MARMADUKE by BRAD ANDERSON
® © 1974 NAT'L. News. Syn.
"I THINK THERE'S A KID UP THERE SHARING HIS LUNCH!"

Marmaduke by BRAD ANDERSON
WAIT 'TIL YOU SEE THE NEW WIG I BOUGHT!
®Tm. Reg. U.S. Pat. Off.—All rights reserved
© 1976 by United Feature Syndicate, Inc.
DOG GONE FUNNY
I THINK SHE'S SAYING 'HEAD 'EM UP AND MOVE 'EM OUT!'
YIP! YIP YIP! YIP! YAHOO YIP
IN ST. PETERSBURG, FLA. A.T. LUBIN SAYS, "When 'BOOFUL', our femme fatale CHIHUAHUA, hears the kitchen dinner call 'SOUPS ON!' she dances, prances, barks and rounds up and herds the household into the dining room!"
GUESS WHO'S GONNA GET A BATH!

Marmaduke by Brad Anderson
LAPPED UP EVERY DROP OF MRS. MABEE'S BRANDIED PEACHES
URP
Tm. Reg. U.S. Pat. Off.—All rights reserved © 1976 by United Feature Syndicate, Inc.
DOG GONE FUNNY
TWEEEEEEEEEE
PANT PANT
PAUL JORDAN FROM AYLMER, ONTARIO, SAYS HIS GERMAN SHEPHERD, 'SHEP,' COMES A'RUNNING WHEN HE HEARS THE TEAKETTLE BOILING BECAUSE HE KNOWS HE WILL GET A CUP OF TEA AND A DOG BISCUIT!
NOW WHAT'S HIS PROBLEM?
AROOF RUF RUF
IT'S FOR YOU!
Marmaduke by Brad Anderson
Tm. Reg. U.S. Pat. Off.—All rights reserved © 1976 by United Feature Syndicate, Inc.
CIRCUS TODAY
"... THEN HE'LL DO A DOUBLE TWIST AND TRIPLE SOMERSAULT BEFORE HE LANDS IN THE GREGORY'S POOL TWO BLOCKS AWAY!"
Lemonade 5¢ 5¢
ICE COLD Lemonade 5¢
"OH, OH! WE JUST WENT BANKRUPT!"
DOG GONE FUNNY
WHO'S DRIVING?
SHARON GOODHEAD LIVES IN NORTH MIAMI BEACH, FLORIDA AND HAS A POODLE NAMED 'MICHELLE'. HER POODLE LOVES TO RIDE A BICYCLE. SHE PUTS HER PAWS ON THE HANDLEBARS AND SITS ON SHARON'S LAP... AND AWAY THEY GO!
NOW THAT YOU'VE CAUGHT IT, WHAT ARE YOU GOING TO DO WITH IT?

Recently I was very flattered when a little girl wrote that she had named her puppy, a Chihuahua, Marmaduke. It seems that people who enjoy reading "Marmaduke" find they relate to him in a very real way. They identify Marmaduke with their dog and it doesn't matter if they own the tiniest poodle or largest hound, the cartoon hits a responsive chord and they let me know with their letters, cards and photos. Sometimes these letters serve as a basis for a cartoon, but more than likely they will end up in the little "DOGGONE FUNNY" cartoon found at the end of each Sunday page comic strip.

Although the daily comic panel first appeared in 1954, it wasn't until 1971 that National Newspaper Syndicate gave the go-ahead on a color comic Sunday page. The Sunday page format has undergone several changes since it first appeared. In the beginning it was a full-sized comic strip, but later was reduced in size when the newsprint shortage hit. Still later, in this reduced size, the format was changed from a comic strip to a grouping of individual cartoons, similar to the individual daily cartoon.

In 1976, "Marmaduke" became a part of the United Feature Syndicate family of comics and the format turned full-circle and went back to the original comic strip. This format has proved most popular.

Alice had a winning smile.

As one leafs through this book, it becomes obvious that the art has changed through the years. But more

Gypsy decided to give us a little surprise . . . nine little surprises to be exact.

than just the art style has changed. I've found it fun to change the style of clothing, hairdos, cars, and to keep up with trends or fads. Dogs aren't easily influenced by fads but sometimes they are easily shocked or confused by us faddish humans. This was shown one Sunday when Phil grew his moustache (page 56), or when the whole family went "mod" a few years ago (page 54).

Writing "Marmaduke" gags is fun. I try to keep it looking fresh each day and it takes a good memory not to repeat oneself after all these years. I also have the assistance of a small but excellent group of professional writers and the invaluable assistance of my oldest son, Craig, who writes and is involved in other phases of cartooning.

My own gag-writing efforts have been assisted by our numerous pets. Three of our favorite dogs have unknowingly helped in the production of the cartoons with their ridiculous poses or antics. Our dogs have consisted of many "Heinz 57" varieties, plus a Lab named Gypsy and two Dalmatians, Duchess and Alice.

Gypsy pulled the greatest trick of all by giving birth to nine puppies while we were on vacation visiting my parents in Jamestown. Our return trip to California was pure joy for the kids, and Gypsy and her pups loved all the attention. Fortunately, we were driving a station wagon and the rear compartment made a fine nursery.

Alice, our Dalmatian, had the ability to smile with a big, broad, toothy grin when she was happy. I've used her smiles and grins in the "Marmaduke" cartoon many times. She loved everything that lived and when Mama Kitty had kittens, Alice would try to mother them. When it was time to give the kittens away, Mama was only slightly upset but poor Alice was heartbroken.

Duchess was a happy clown and I've thought about

her many times while drawing a particularly funny situation. She loved to swim. We had a stream running past our property in New York state. On warm summer days, Duchess would go splashing up and down its length raising a wall of water on both sides as she ran. Our neighbor, whose house bordered on the creek, said she was sure she could hear Duchess happily chuckling and laughing as she tore through the creek.

When we lived in Vista, we had a big shade tree in the backyard. It was one of my favorite places for dreaming up ideas. One day, while I was sitting there sketching ideas, Alice came out and lay down beside my chair. Soon little Dazy lay down beside Alice. Then our cat, Mama, walked over and lay down beside Dazy. Mama had a mouse in her mouth. She put the mouse down on the ground between her paws . . . and there we all sat. I managed to come up with some pretty good gag situations that day, and after about an hour I got up and left. I never saw the mouse again.

Brad acquires a very strange audience while sketching Marmaduke Sunday pages.

"If somebody doesn't call for him soon, I'm putting in for early retirement!"

"Phil, I think Billy and Marmaduke are beginning to have too strong an effect on each other!"

"It's a good thing you asked me to help! Bathing Marmaduke is A TWO MAN JOB!"

"I don't think Marmaduke's got the hang of it yet!"

"He may not understand the game, but they haven't been able to make a goal in two years!"

"Okay, pooch, that's it . . . 13 rides are ENOUGH for one day!"

"You didn't have to push the button so hard, Marmaduke!"

"I sent YOU in to get HIM out of bed!"

"Don't blame Marmaduke, mom. He thinks they're stealing all our best stuff!"

"See, Billy? Marmaduke didn't mind the medicine, did you, boy?"

"Fellas, there's been a horrible mistake!"

"That's right, ladies . . . Roll over! Again . . . Roll over! Again . . . Roll . . ."

"Now THERE'S a sight we don't see very often!"

"I KNEW one of them would fight back someday!"

"Let ME catch one for a change . . . I'm TIRED of just writing out the ticket!"

"Phil, come right over! I'd like to get something off my chest!"

"I'll take back that remote control if you don't mind!"

"Well, there's another sports car driver who won't blow his horn at him!"

"See, Mom? I told you he wouldn't track up your clean floor!"

"We sent him to an obedience school and he organized their first campus riot!"

"Marmaduke likes his teddy bear when it's storming!"

"Quick!! Where's the fuse?!"

"You were supposed to WAIT TILL I LIT THE CANDLES, Marmaduke!"

"Keep your follow-the-leader games outdoors!"

"Forget it, Marmaduke! . . . It's NOT going to drip!"

"Could one of THESE be yours, officer?"

"The only way to save is to cut HIM down to five meals a day!"

"It's too good to be true! He finally dug a hole so deep, even HE can't get out!"

"Keep calm, Martha! He likes his tea WITHOUT sugar!"

"Nothing like a cold nose to get a person up in the morning, is there?"

The tips of his ears get cold!

"Are you sure you'll still love me if I take it from you?"

"When I volunteered to take charge of extra-curricular activities, I didn't expect HIM!"

"Oh, dear! I forgot to warn the ladies church committee about you!"

"Sorry, he can't go out with you boys tonight!"

...I said to bring in your FATHER!"

"Sorry -- we cater only to customers with money!"

"I feel ridiculous when he ESCORTS us through the tougher neighborhoods."

"And at the HEAD of the table, no less!"

"Wake up Phil! There's a burglar hiding under the bed."

"I'm always glad when marble season comes -- it gets him out of the house."

"Who's telling this fish story, anyway?!"

"Maybe he's really a handsome prince that can only be awakened by a kiss from a pretty girl."

"Stop trying to look cute when I'm telling someone what a pain in the neck you are!"

"If you think THAT'S funny, you should see him trying to communicate with a tankful of tropical fish!"

"Can I get you anything to spice up my slipper. . . salt, pepper ketchup?"

"When are you going to GRADUATE?"

"Where did I put that hypodermic needle?"

"One thing about taking Marmaduke along on a picnic. . . you appreciate the ants."

"Wonder if Winslow will make his turn at the car pool today. Last night he said his car wouldn't start."

"I'll hear Dottie's side of it first."

"Ok, so you brought my slippers. Stop hamming it! They didn't taste that bad!"

"It's the game of the week."

"He ordered pepperoni. . . "

"So that's why our new neighbors say we're nosy."

"Forget about getting even with that highway department asphalt truck."

"You oughta see the way Marmaduke is fixin' up his doghouse!"

"Can't we have some kind of rule about members wagging their tails inside the tent?"

"Hey, Al, we got a catcher's mitt for a left-handed Great Dane?"

"He sat on my balloon!"

"Put it in the pile in the corner . . . he now has 175 bones on deposit."

"They've got to be kidding! Come on, let's ring the bell."

"Call the police! Lock me in a cell! I demand my rights!"

"You don't often see a reunion like this."

"And I suppose you'd like me to serve milk and cookies, too?"

"But, Daddy, it's HIS pool party!"

"That reminds me, Marjorie, when are you putting up drapes at this window?"

"As of now, Marmaduke, you are no longer a member of the pirate raft crew!"

"Keep your eyes open for a big dog. He's a real trouble-maker."

"There was this big hairy guy, and he started chasin' Marmaduke with his motorcycle. . ."

"He decided to go through a car wash."

"Mom, will you make Marmaduke quit rescuing me every five minutes?"

"Help! (yawn) Help! (yawn) I'm being robbed."

"He remembers the candy you gave him when he was a puppy."

"It's times like this I wish I'd stayed in law school."

"Marmaduke took the paper in for you Pop. It is in the living room, and kitchen, and bedroom and. . .

"That short circuit in the electric blanket last week has certainly made a difference in the way Marmaduke wakes me up."

"The gas company assigns only its best jumpers to the Marmaduke neighborhood!"

"Get a firm grip on your seats, everyone. Billy forgot his lunch again!"

"What are we supposed to do. . .bark?!"

"Cheer up, fella. . .an intercepted pass is one of the hazards of this game."

"Uh. . .let's wait 'till we find a trash can. . ."

"Did you ever see such raw courage?"

"Never, Snyder, NEVER call him a 'great dame.'"

"Why isn't it petty, childish, and ridiculous for him to steal my chair instead of sprawling on the sofa!"

"I'll be glad when this school talent show is over!"

"The safest thing to do is to assume he got a large inheritance and can afford to buy it."

"Mr. Snyder sure has changed. He wasn't mad at all when his paint bucket fell over."

"It's alright, Aunt Mae. He'll stop when he gets to your shoulder!"

"Must you always send Marmaduke to remind me that I forgot to kiss you goodbye?"

"This is the part of the day I dread most . . .getting home!"

"One soap opera nut was ENOUGH!"

"How many times have I told you not to play with the faucets when you want a drink?"

"He doesn't seem to want to go out tonight!"

"He's forging a northwest passage to the front door."

"I WOULD get traffic duty only two blocks from YOUR house!"

"He saw one on T.V."

"What a time to get friendly!"

"Sit there for a while. . . I want to see how many complaints YOU get!"

"There now, are you satisfied that there's nothing wrong with him?"

"I don't think this is necessary every time you bring your friends to the house."

"You're exhausting my reservoir of good will!"

"Forgive the way the place looks. Marmaduke is taking inventory."

"Is there some harmless way you could cause a pest to go 'poof' and just disappear?"

"Who put this beatup bone in the stew?"

"Oh, no, not another football game!"

"I hate to think what is going to happen to the poor cuckoo bird when he pops out this time!"

"It's a list of demands that says we discriminate against furry four-legged people."

"What in heck is going on here?"

"I don't care how cold your ears get! That's my new wig!"

"Watch it — they're trying a flying wedge!"

"What IS this? A day-care center?"

"Tell Mr. Snyder to pull the drapes and look out the window at what we made for him."

"Oh, yes. I think your new perfume smells wonderful."

"Lois, what was the name and address of those people at camp who had the big dog?"

"Be careful.. If a ball rolls into the street around here, it's followed by a 200-pound dog."

"Sure he likes the blindfold test. . .that way he gets to eat ALL THREE brands!"

"Meow, meow, fsssst! fsssst! Sic'm, Marmaduke, sic'm!"

"It's o.k., lady, Marmaduke doesn't care if your baby plays with his old bone!"

"What's so weird about cooling off on a hot day?"

"You can take it off when she leaves, but Aunt Martha is going to see you wearing the rhinestone collar she gave you!"

"So that's where our door mat vanished to!"

"No, I'm not looking for tonsils. . .I think he ate my stethoscope."

"You're bestowing an honor upon me, I suppose?"

"I don't care what you say, Jack. If he wants to walk at 5 m.p.h., then I'm going to drive at 5 m.p.h."

"You scare him when your face gets all purple an' red an' mad-looking like that!"

"It's a pleasure to meet someone these days who just listens!"

"You'll just have to get another cart for the groceries, Phil."

"Has anyone seen my toothbrush?"

"A root beer float for me, and a steak for my friend here."

"This always happens when he looks at Billy's comic books."

"Mommy, is the baby's bottle warm now?"

"We appreciate your keeping him company all day, but..."

"Remember the contact shelf paper you bought? Well, Marmaduke found it!"

"Marmaduke wants in! That last clap of thunder did it!"

"Next time maybe you won't get mad and throw Marmaduke's ball up on the roof!"

"Why Phil, Marmaduke's been home for half an hour!"

"You've got to stop licking dogfood commercials!"

"But it's only a slightly cheaper brand!"

"Did I say STRIKE? How ridiculous of me! Of course I meant BALL!"

"No wonder we were cold during the night!"

"I don't know where he lives, but he shows up with his dish every time we have a cookout."

"We were having a wonderful time, but that wasn't good enough for you! You had to stir up some excitement!"

"Now you're afraid to let go of it, aren't you?"

"How much longer are you going to carry on this strip-mining operation?"

"That's Dottie's first move in cleaning the house."

"Carrying the telephone book won't get you into school."

"He keeps trying to get the last bark!"

"How would you two like your eggs this morning... besides cracked right on your heads?"

"We find we collect THREE times as much as we used to!"

"I guess you'd better turn around!"

"Well, folks, it looks like we're going to get one dog's opinion whether we want it or not!"

"Marmaduke has a hobby...getting into trouble."

"He's saying hello!"

"He always does that after barking all day."

"I wish you two would snore in the same key!"

"I can't imagine how this found its way into the fondue pot, can you dear?"

"Would you believe a thorn in the paw could deserve so much attention?"

"He means well."

"He wouldn't let us neglect him even if we wanted to!"

" We gave up years ago trying to convince him he was a dog! "

"Wouldn't you know he'd be the only one with a perfect attendance record?"

"Can't you ever wade in a little at a time?"

"Go chase the bone, Marmaduke!"

"Why does he always have to take a nap the same time I do?"

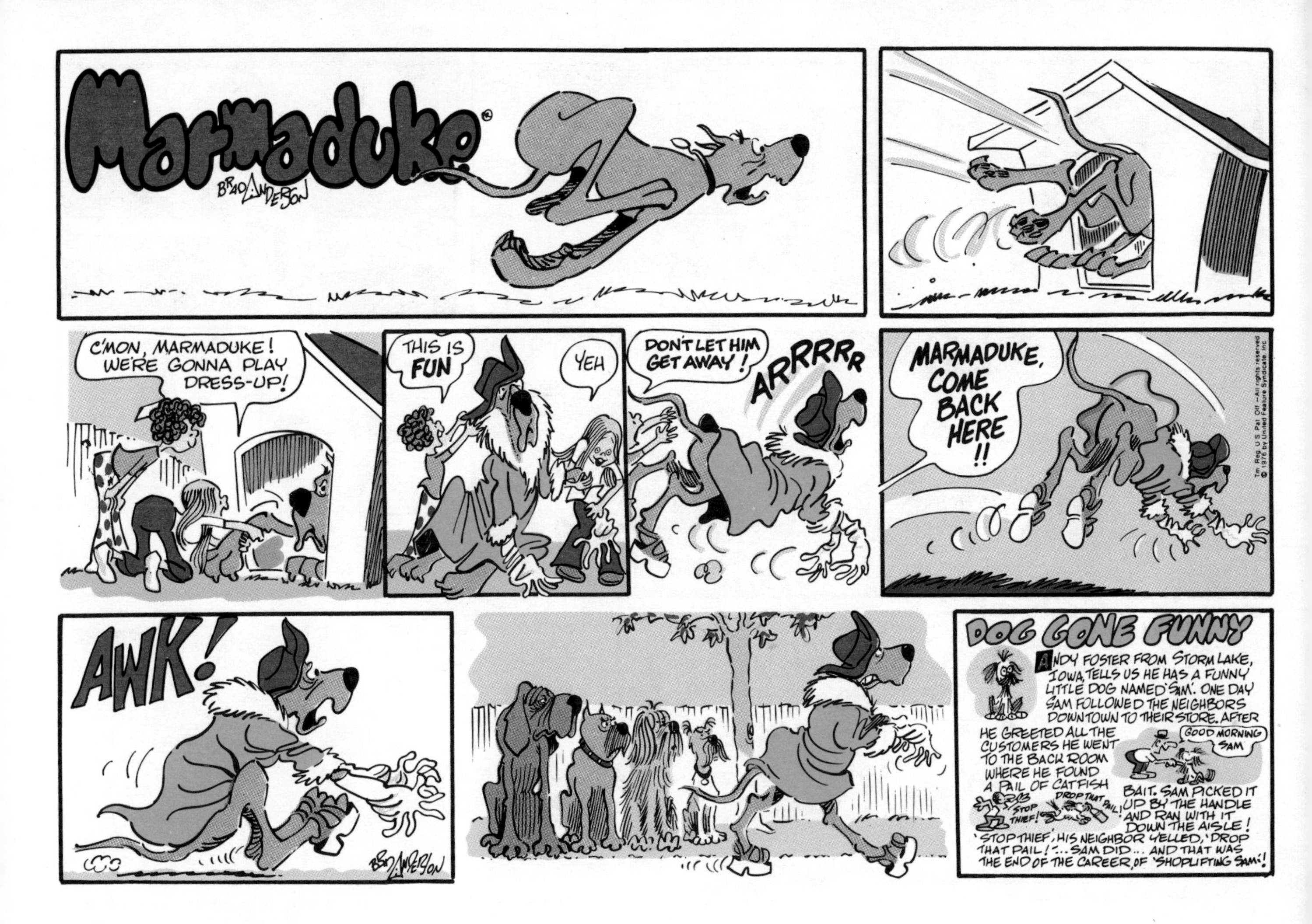
Marmaduke®
BRAD ANDERSON
C'MON, MARMADUKE! WE'RE GONNA PLAY DRESS-UP!
THIS IS FUN
YEH
DON'T LET HIM GET AWAY!
ARRRRRR
MARMADUKE, COME BACK HERE!!
Tm. Reg. U.S. Pat. Off.—All rights reserved © 1976 by United Feature Syndicate, Inc.
AWK!
BRAD ANDERSON
DOG GONE FUNNY
ANDY FOSTER FROM STORM LAKE, IOWA, TELLS US HE HAS A FUNNY LITTLE DOG NAMED 'SAM'. ONE DAY SAM FOLLOWED THE NEIGHBORS DOWNTOWN TO THEIR STORE. AFTER HE GREETED ALL THE CUSTOMERS HE WENT TO THE BACK ROOM WHERE HE FOUND A PAIL OF CATFISH BAIT. SAM PICKED IT UP BY THE HANDLE AND RAN WITH IT DOWN THE AISLE! 'STOP THIEF', HIS NEIGHBOR YELLED, 'DROP THAT PAIL!'... SAM DID... AND THAT WAS THE END OF THE CAREER, OF 'SHOPLIFTING SAM'!
GOOD MORNING SAM
STOP THIEF!
DROP THAT PAIL!

GALUB
GOO
GALOO
GLUB
GLAG
GLUG
GAR
BLAB
WAAAAA
Tm. Reg. U.S. Pat. Off.—All rights reserved © 1977 by United Feature Syndicate, Inc.
BOP
BOP
SIGH
BRAD ANDERSON
DOG GONE FUNNY
SUSAN JOHNSON FROM VANCOUVER, B.C., SAYS HER COLLIE, 'SNOOPY', TRIED TO ROUND UP ALL HER UNCLES CHICKENS WHEN THEY VISITED HIS FARM IN SASKATCHEWAN! 'SNOOPY' ALSO LOVES TO PLAY IN THE WATER, BUT HATES TO TAKE A BATH!

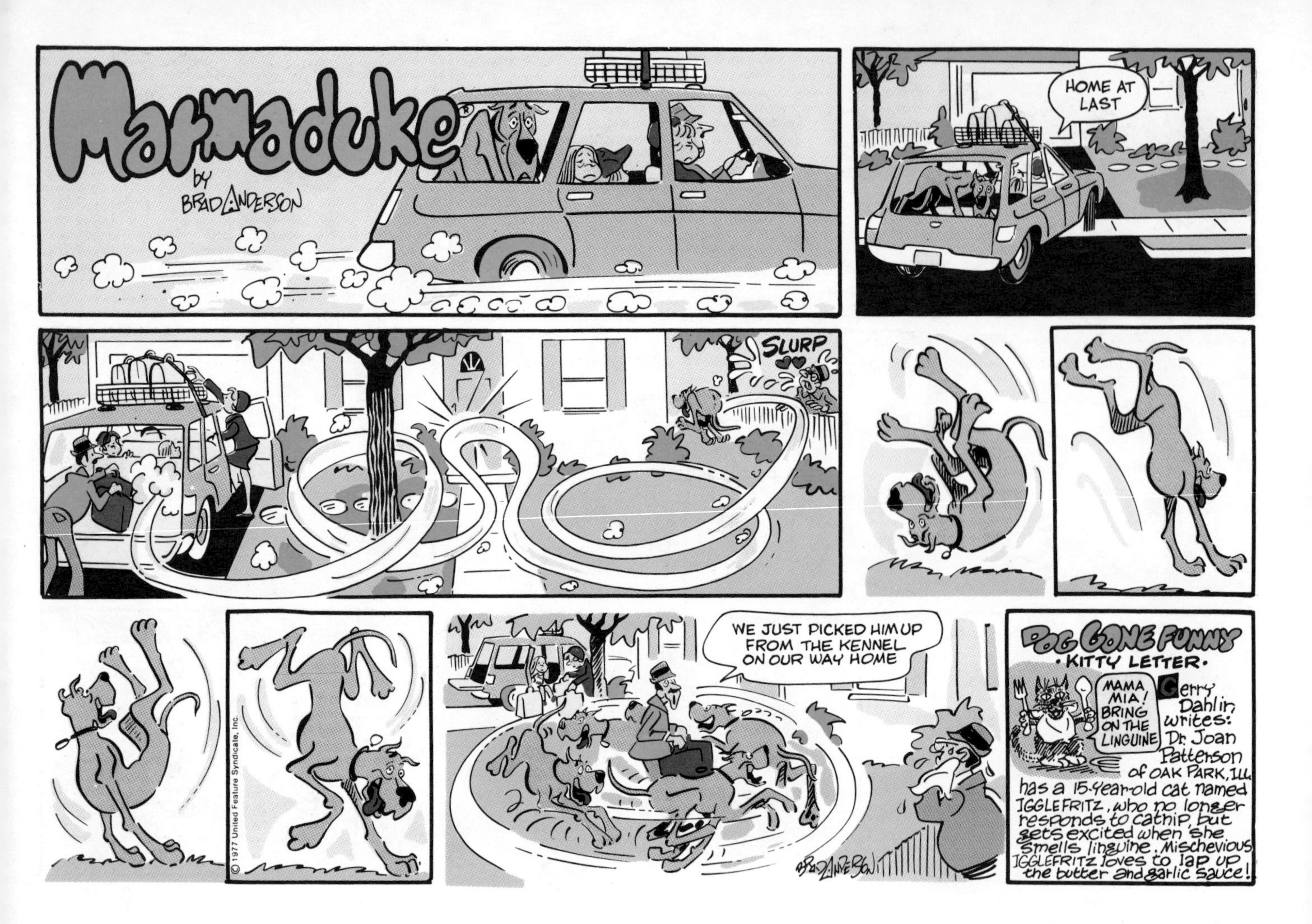
Marmaduke
by
BRAD ANDERSON
HOME AT LAST
SLURP
© 1977 United Feature Syndicate, Inc.
WE JUST PICKED HIM UP FROM THE KENNEL ON OUR WAY HOME
BRAD ANDERSON
DOG GONE FUNNY
·KITTY LETTER·
MAMA MIA! BRING ON THE LINGUINE
Gerry Dahlin writes: Dr. Joan Patterson of OAK PARK, ILL. has a 15-year-old cat named IGGLEFRITZ, who no longer responds to catnip, but gets excited when she smells linguine. Mischevious IGGLEFRITZ loves to lap up the butter and garlic sauce!

STEAK BITS
STEAK BITS
STEAK BITS
© 1977 United Feature Syndicate, Inc.
3-20
BRAD ANDERSON
DOG GONE FUNNY
WHO ATE MY SALAD?
Minnie Bradigan, from Forestville, N.Y., had a dog that loved salads with salad dressing!

Marmaduke®
MARMADUKE
?
MARMADUKE
HISSSSSS
PHHTTT
PHHTTT
PHHTTT PHHTTT
© 1977 United Feature Syndicate, Inc.
HISS
PHHTT
PHHHT
MARMADUKE
2-3
BRAD ANDERSON
DOG GONE FUNNY
'KITTY LETTER'
HE CLAIMS IT'S BETTER THAN CATNIP!
WHAT WILL THE OTHER CATS IN SPANAWAY, WASH. THINK?
Marla Williams wrote to MARMADUKE: "we have a cat named KIPPER. For some reason he loves to sniff birdseed. He loves it so much he climbs onto our birdhouse and has a ball sniffing it!!

MY DOG IS NAMED MARMADUKE... WHAT'S HIS NAME ?
IT'S NOT A HIM!
Tm. Reg. U.S. Pat. Off.—All rights reserved © 1976 by United Feature Syndicate, Inc.
HER NAME IS LADY!
OH, FOR GOODNESS SAKE!
C'MON, MARMADUKE!
WE GOTTA GET YOU SOME GLASSES!
BRAD ANDERSON
DOG GONE FUNNY
AMEN
ARF
MRS EVELYN TALLY WRITES FROM YUCAIPA, CALIF. "WHEN WE GO TO PRAY, OUR TOY FOX TERRIER 'SNOOPY' GETS DOWN BESIDE US AND CROSSES HIS PAWS LIKE HE IS PRAYING, TOO!!

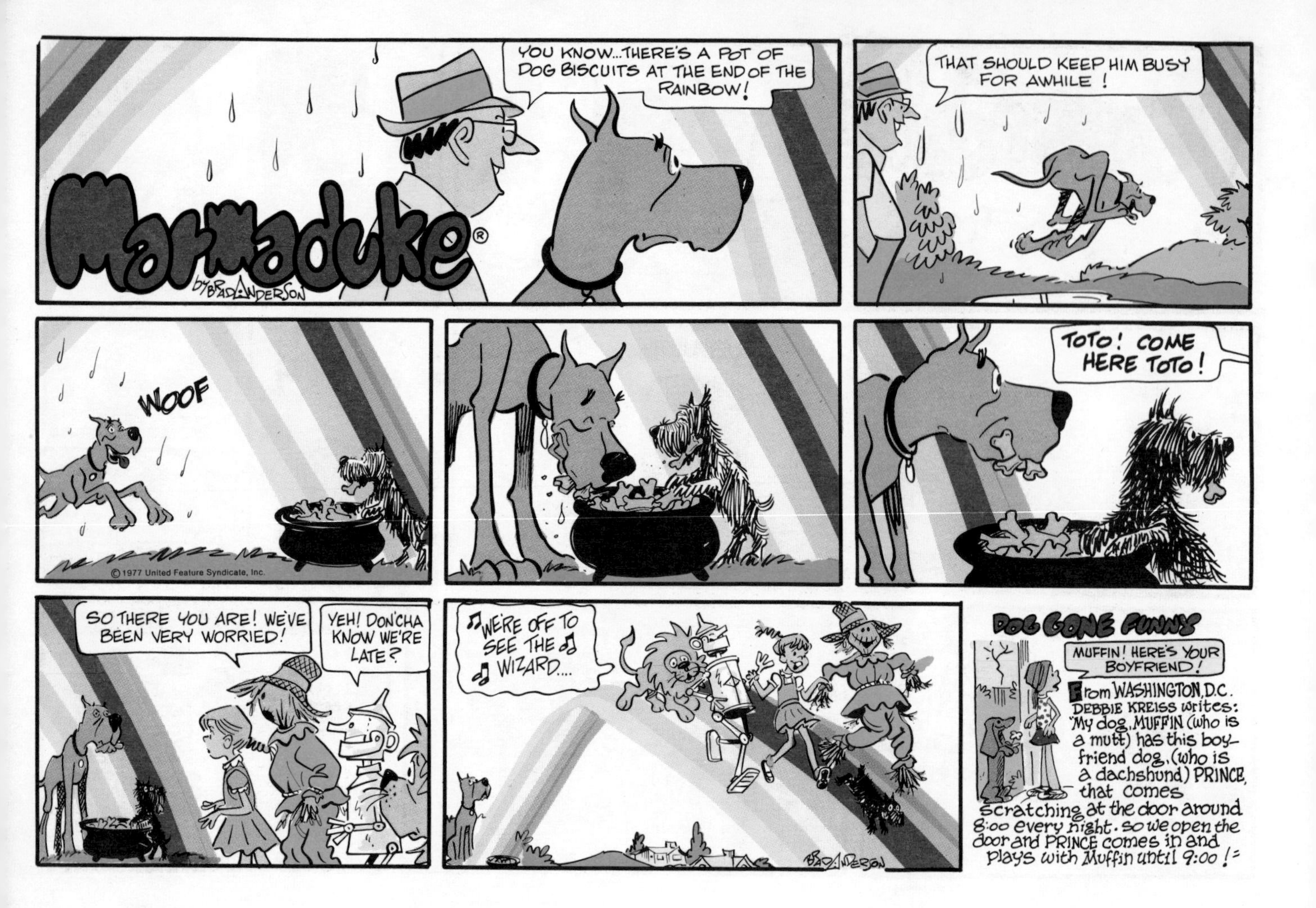
Marmaduke
by BRAD ANDERSON
YOU KNOW...THERE'S A POT OF DOG BISCUITS AT THE END OF THE RAINBOW!
THAT SHOULD KEEP HIM BUSY FOR AWHILE!
WOOF
© 1977 United Feature Syndicate, Inc.
TOTO! COME HERE TOTO!
SO THERE YOU ARE! WE'VE BEEN VERY WORRIED!
YEH! DON'CHA KNOW WE'RE LATE?
WE'RE OFF TO SEE THE WIZARD....
BRAD ANDERSON
DOG GONE FUNNYS
MUFFIN! HERE'S YOUR BOYFRIEND!
From WASHINGTON, D.C. DEBBIE KREISS writes: "My dog, MUFFIN (who is a mutt) has this boy-friend dog, (who is a dachshund) PRINCE, that comes scratching at the door around 8:00 every night. so we open the door and PRINCE comes in and plays with Muffin until 9:00!"

SIGH
HERE'S OLD MARMADUKE
DOGS ARE LUCKY
THEY DON'T HAVE TO GO TO SCHOOL
BOY, DOES HE HAVE IT EASY
SCHOOL BUS
WHAT FUN THINGS HAVE YOU BEEN DOIN', MARMADUKE?
YEH! JUST PLAY ALL DAY
HI DUKE
NOTHING BUT FUN! FUN! FUN!
Tm. Reg. U.S. Pat. Off.—All rights reserved © 1976 by United Feature Syndicate, Inc.
BRAD ANDERSON
DOG GONE FUNNYS
I WANT TO BE ALONE
GEE! WHAT A SNOB
RANDY LEE WARD WRITES FROM FT. WORTH, TEX. THAT HIS POODLE, FIFI, EATS OUT OF A PAPER BOWL. WHEN HIS SISTER'S DOG, BRANDY, COMES NEAR WHILE SHE'S EATING, FIFI PICKS UP HER BOWL AND HEADS FOR THE BACK DOOR!

Marmaduke®
by BRAD ANDERSON
'SUNDAY FUNNIES'
DADDY!
YEH!
DADDY! READ US THE FUNNIES!
SURE!
COMICS
MARMADUKE LIKES THE FUNNIES TOO!
HEY, MARMADUKE!
OH, NO!
KALUMP
KALUMP
KALUMP
YOU DO IT EVERYTIME!
Tm Reg U S Pat Off - All rights reserved © 1977 by United Feature Syndicate, Inc
JUST GIVE ME ANOTHER PAPER ... NEVER MIND WHY!!
POCKET BOOKS
PIPES
NUTS
CIGARS
BRAD ANDERSON
DOG GONE FUNNY
TIME FOR YOUR NIGHT CAP
JANET S. WATSON FROM BLOOMFIELD HILLS, MICHIGAN, SAYS, "I have an eight-year-old YORKSHIRE TERRIER named 'TWIGGY' who refuses to tuck in at the foot of my bed until she has her nightly treat... A TUMS... which she eats with absolute delight... then she settles down to go to sleep."
NOW THAT'S DOGGONE FUNNY!

HMMM... MILD IRRITATION OF THE THROAT!
© 1977 United Feature Syndicate, Inc.
SOME CONGESTION!
SLIGHT FEVER!
VETERINARY MEDICINE
NOTHING A SHOT WON'T CURE!
VETERINARY MEDICINE
EXCUSE US DOC...
MARMADUKE WANTS A SECOND MEDICAL OPINION!
BRAD ANDERSON
DOG GONE FUNNY
GRRR!
YOU FORGOT TO SAY GRACE!
KATHY ROBINSON in Wyckoff, N.J. says her schnauzer, ROBIN, will lie in front of her dish of food with her head between her paws and refuse to eat until KATHY says the same grace as the ROBINSON family uses before meals!

ALL FINISHED!
JUST ENOUGH TIME TO RUSH TO THE HAIR DRESSER
Marmaduke
by BRAD ANDERSON
GUARD THE HOUSE MARMADUKE
HEY, MOM! CAN WE HAVE SOMETHING TO EAT?
OH, BOY!
CHOCOLATE CAKE!
TWO PIECES, PLEASE
OKAY!
YEH!
MY FAVORITE
MINE TOO!
?
© 1977 United Feature Syndicate, Inc.
MAR MA DUKE!
BRAD ANDERSON
DOG GONE FUNNY
MRS HAZEL GIBIS of St Paul, Minn. has grandsons Vince, Mark and Brock, whose dog buries pancakes...NOT bones! He digs them up and eats them later!

DON'T YOU KNOW A DOG'S PLACE IS ON THE FLOOR AT HIS MASTER'S FEET?
DAILY
HERE... I'LL SHOW YOU!
© 1977 United Feature Syndicate, Inc.
GETTING THE IDEA?
ZZZZZZZ
ZZZZ
ZZZZ
I SUPPOSE IT HAS SOMETHING TO DO WITH EQUAL RIGHTS FOR DOGS!
BRAD ANDERSON
DOG GONE FUNNY
EMPTY, AGAIN?
From BUFFALO, N.Y. M.Whalen writes that their old dog, TINA, would bring her water bowl to be filled when it was empty! Whalen's present dog, TIPPY, dines only in the dining room! ALTHO she is fed in the kitchen, she carries each mouthful to the dining room!

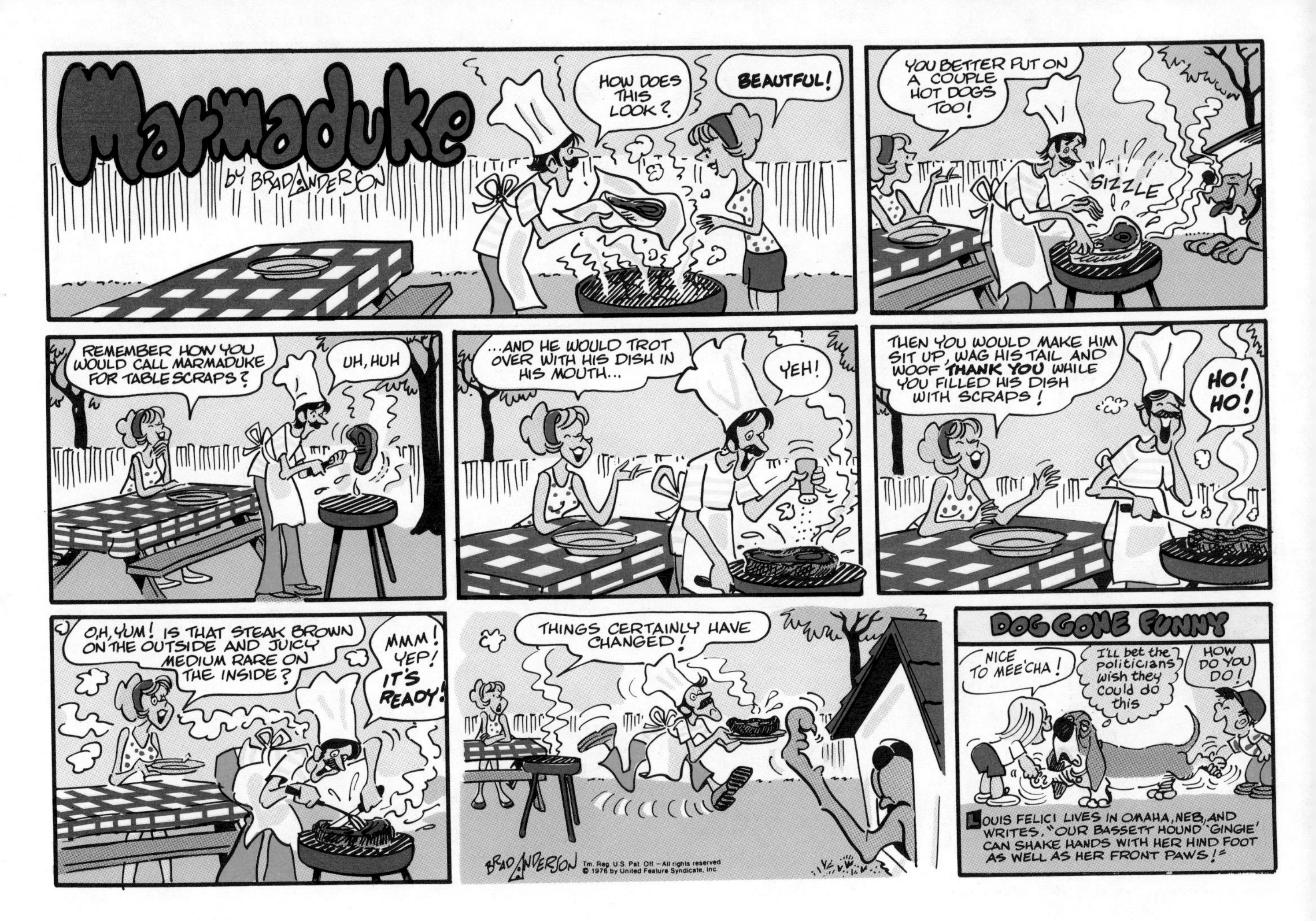
Marmaduke
by BRAD ANDERSON
HOW DOES THIS LOOK?
BEAUTFUL!
YOU BETTER PUT ON A COUPLE HOT DOGS TOO!
SIZZLE
REMEMBER HOW YOU WOULD CALL MARMADUKE FOR TABLE SCRAPS?
UH, HUH
...AND HE WOULD TROT OVER WITH HIS DISH IN HIS MOUTH...
YEH!
THEN YOU WOULD MAKE HIM SIT UP, WAG HIS TAIL AND WOOF THANK YOU WHILE YOU FILLED HIS DISH WITH SCRAPS!
HO! HO!
OH, YUM! IS THAT STEAK BROWN ON THE OUTSIDE AND JUICY MEDIUM RARE ON THE INSIDE?
MMM! YEP! IT'S READY!
THINGS CERTAINLY HAVE CHANGED!
BRAD ANDERSON
Tm. Reg. U.S. Pat. Off.—All rights reserved © 1976 by United Feature Syndicate, Inc.
DOG GONE FUNNY
NICE TO MEE'CHA!
I'll bet the politicians wish they could do this
HOW DO YOU DO!
LOUIS FELICI LIVES IN OMAHA, NEB, AND WRITES, "OUR BASSETT HOUND 'GINGIE' CAN SHAKE HANDS WITH HER HIND FOOT AS WELL AS HER FRONT PAWS!"

MARMADUKE!
STAY!
STOP
COME BACK HERE!
SIT!
SIT!
DO YOU HEAR
PUFF PUFF
ME?
COME HERE!
PHIL!
MARMADUKE!
SUPPER!
© 1977 United Feature Syndicate, Inc.
SCREEECH!
WHY DIDN'T I THINK OF THAT?
BRAD ANDERSON
DOG GONE FUNNY
Paula Doyle from EVERETT, Mass., says her dog KELLY can SPELL! He loves to go for walks so much that all Paula has to do is spell the word W-A-L-K and KELLY comes running, jumping and wagging his tail.

Marmaduke
by BRAD ANDERSON
SPLAT!
RRUMBUMBUM
BUM
BUM
RUMBUMBLE
BUM
BOOM
BUM
BUM
© 1977 United Feature Syndicate, Inc.
BOOM
BUM
BOOM
BUM BUM
MEOW
MEW
YOU'D THINK THAT DOG WOULD HAVE ENOUGH SENSE TO GET OUT OF THE RAIN!
BRAD ANDERSON
DOG GONE FUNNY
FOXY, a 1 ft. tall, 12 lb. (soaking wet) mixed terrier belongs to ELAINE DRAPER from W. Bloomfield, Mich. FOXY climbs trees, ladders and slides down Playground slides! When ELAINE goes swimming FOXY will swim all over the lake with the gang, and fences can't keep him in or out because he can jump six feet high!

NO CHARGE FOR YOU BILLY
TOLL GATE
STOP AND PAY TOLL
YEH! FREE!
1¢
HI BILLY!
HI
I'LL MOVE THAT WAGON BILLY!
THANKS
HI BILLY!
HI BILLY!
HI BILLY!
HI BILLY!
HI
I DON'T KNOW WHY EVERYBODY SAYS THOSE KIDS ON THE OTHER BLOCK ARE SO TOUGH...
© 1977 United Feature Syndicate, Inc.
THEY'RE ALWAYS NICE TO ME!
BRAD ANDERSON
DOG GONE FUNNY
Sherry Bosko, from Selkirk, Manitoba says her dog Dino has his own security blanket. He even sleeps with it in his mouth!

Every cartoonist should have an assistant like this.

Speaking as a pet owner, I know that a dog can express its feelings and its moments of happiness, joy, or hurt in its own unique way. I try to capture some of these feelings in my cartoons. I don't think every "Marmaduke" cartoon or Sunday page must produce a belly laugh in the traditional comic sense. I like to think Marmaduke is sometimes very much like a circus clown, allowing us to both laugh and sympathize with him while we hurt and laugh at the same time. Sometimes his doleful clownlike expression tells it all.

Every "Marmaduke" cartoon is a lively situation. Even when he is sleeping, something is happening or about to happen. I don't care too much for cartoon panels with static situations, where two people are just talking or explaining what is happening. In fact, who needs the cartoon? Not only is competition among newspaper comic features very strong, we also face competition from television. So I try my best to grab the reader's eye by having "Marmaduke" in action every day.

Through the years, as I drew "Marmaduke," the character began to grow . . . and not just in size! He actually began growing inside me. He took possession, so to speak, when I would sit down at the drawing board and begin to draw. I would find that I actually felt his moments of joy or sadness or embarrassment. The emotion would flow from my brush to the paper without conscious effort. In fact, Barbara said I made so many

Brad says sometimes Marmaduke literally leaps off the drawing board.

funny faces while drawing "Marmaduke" that we had a mirror installed in my studio. I don't know if it helps, but I get to look at a funny face every day.

I suppose everyone has heard the expression, "My dog acts so human he can almost talk." That's the feeling I try to express in each cartoon, and that's why Marmaduke never speaks. His expressions speak for him. Marmaduke's face expresses all of his emotions. His ears and mouth play their part, but the eyes are the single most important element. When we look at his eyes we know exactly what he's trying to tell us.

As I went through the cartoons for this book, it became obvious that Marmaduke, as a character, had changed over the years. In the beginning, he seemed to view the world with a steadfast scowl of superiority. However, he has mellowed with time and this has permitted me to give added dimension to what began as a simple dog cartoon.

Drawing a daily cartoon or a Sunday page has become a very involved process for me. In the beginning, I was primarily interested in presenting a well-constructed, funny, one-panel cartoon. Technique was very important.

Today, I'm not concerned with technique so much as I am concerned with keeping the artwork legible when it is reduced. Most newspapers can't afford to give the space to comics that they did a few years ago and, as a result, comic strips and panels are sometimes reduced and squeezed into a very small area. The finished artwork must take these extreme reductions into account, so the artwork must be bold yet simple enough to hold together. A small cartoon panel, as opposed to a strip, can very easily become lost on a newspaper page. Fortunately, Marmaduke is a very large character and this helps make it easier to find him on a busy page.

Barb handles all the mechanical tasks and errands.

I do all the artwork from layout to finished inking and lettering. However, there are certain necessary mechanical processes and my wife, Barbara, handles these. She also takes care of trips to the printers, sorting fan mail, answering requests, and other necessary chores connected with the production of a daily comic feature. She is my best critic and when I'm not sure about a certain cartoon, I show it to her. I have been known to do a complete Sunday page over after showing it to her.

The daily comic format hasn't changed since the beginning. It's still drawn in a square box. The original drawing measures 7½ x 7½ inches. Using a ballpoint pen,

I draw a rough sketch on a sheet of 8½ x 11-inch newsprint. Sometimes I will make several sketches and then pick the one that best suits the gag situation I have in mind.

I then take the rough sketch and tape it to the underside of a sheet of one-ply Grumbacher's plate finish Bristol board. I place this on a light board, which consists of a piece of frosted glass with a light under it. Using a No. 1 Winsor & Newton brush I ink directly on the Bristol board without any further penciling. This method not only gives me a clean finished drawing without erasures, it also gives me a lot of freedom when I make the drawing. As a result, the finished drawing is more spontaneous than it would be if I were just trying to fill in the penciled lines. Many cartoonists employ artists who do the final inking on their strips or panels, but I prefer to do my own inking. I feel this makes a considerable contribution to the character of the artwork.

I suppose "Marmaduke" is a very simple cartoon. There are no great philosophical thoughts, no political comments, no stinging put-downs, and no insults. I'd rather look for something funny, or tender, in our daily relationships with our dogs and pets. These cartoons will never be considered great cartoon art or humor, but I hope they will inspire some small child to want to read or comfort an older person who can no longer afford the companionship of a pet, and, most of all, I hope they will make you, the reader, laugh.

"Marmaduke" is twenty-four years old this year and has appeared in more than seven thousand daily comic panels and Sunday page strips. Not only is this the best way I can think of to make a living, you might also say I just work for the fun of it.

I hope you have enjoyed watching Marmaduke "grow up" as much as I have enjoyed presenting him to you.

Marmaduke has a better idea.

"Nobody invited you to tea!"

"'cause I'd rather dance with Marmaduke than some dumb old girl!"

"We gave up the training program. He had us obeying his every whim!"

"It's okay, mom. He's taking over for the postman after the skate board mishap!"

"I'm afraid that technically he is on a leash."

"I wonder if we could interest him in having a garage sale?"

"Mom . . . Marmaduke did it again!"

"He showed me some new shortcuts today!"

"Cease fire!"

"Little old ladies sure don't have to worry with him around."

" You wait up for him, and don't take any flimsy excuses about why he is late! "

" There MUST be something wrong. I told him to SIT and he SAT! "

"Marmaduke had a bad day at school!"

"This is disgraceful! Where have you been?"

"He's bluffing! He could never go on a hunger strike!"

"Tackle him! Tackle him! Tackle him!"

"What strange noise have you heard tonight?"

"No wonder Jessup gets credit for more arrests than we do!"

"Phil! This turkey will need a bodyguard for a few minutes."

"Dottie, I've uncovered the mystery of the missing bedspread."

"He responds to 'Down, Boy!', but he takes you down with him!"

"Actually, I've heard that a quick dash now and then is very good for the old circulation."

"This has been a great day! Blue skies, soft summer air and I haven't seen Marmaduke since morning!"

"Dottie! Where's my pipe?"

"Will you stop eating that popcorn, so I can hear the news?"

"A creature from outer space? That's what I've always figured."

"Ham it up all you want, you're not getting an air conditioner!"

"Boy, I'd hide too!"

"You're supposed to sprawl at your master's feet, not on his lap!"

"No, he won't roll over or sit. Now he wants to know if you do any tricks."

"He isn't my dog. I thought he was yours."

"Are YOU the lady of the house?"

"Shall we dance?"

"You're a naughty dog!"

"Phil, do something! He's already drunk half the water!"

"He saw the price of dog food."

"Phil, the dog-catcher is after Marma...

...forget it!"

"Whatsamatter? He's a real good kisser!"

"He went chasing after the chuck wagon in the dog food commercial!"

"You know how to wake him, don't you? Just try to grab one of his bones!"

"This free meal you promised them. Where's it coming from?"

"We don't want to insult him, so just tell him he's over-qualified."

"Stop struggling, Marmaduke. You're supposed to be an UNCONSCIOUS accident victim!"

"Hey! I thought possession was nine tenths of the law."

"Don't be fooled by that hungry look on his face. He can turn it on and off!"

"I don't think that is one bit funny, Phil!"

"Really, Marmaduke! I don't need any coaching advice!"

"Dottie! Who's been into my strawberry wine?"

"What is he doing? Surveying his kingdom?"

"I didn't THINK that sounded like Phil's usual morning grunt!"

"Now do you believe there isn't any mail for you?"

"Why do your hunger pains always come at the most critical point in the game?"

"Why is he your dog when he's good, and mine when he gets into trouble?"

"At least he liked the steak."

"This is not a watering hole!"

"Day after day that same dog stands at the window and drools!"

"When Phil tells a joke, Al... you laugh!"

"Marmaduke! How many times must I tell you dogs don't have pets!"

"I think it's known as squatter's rights."

"I thought <u>everybody</u> liked Frank Sinatra!"

"He doesn't approve of smoking!"

"She says her name is Lisa and she's hijacking Marmaduke to her house!"

"Help! He's after the lemon meringue pie!"

"So that's how he gets in after we've gone to bed."

"A fool and his bone are soon parted."

"I told you Marmaduke didn't like to be ignored."

"Periodically we have to get rid of the stuff Marmaduke drags home!"

"Guess who teacher picked to be the Big Bad Wolf in the school play . . ."

"I'm all for a car pool, but do we have to drop him off at school every morning?"

"... now move the other foot!"

"C'mon! Somebody remember the password!"

"When Marmaduke's tail starts to wag, you know an ice cream truck is on its way!"

"This isn't exactly the place I wanted to give a demonstration, lady."

"I know you ate my candy bar 'cause you got chocolate breath!"

"Didn't you know? The sightseeing bus goes by our house now."

"Friend of the bride!"

"I know Marmaduke tears up your lawn, but remember all the times he's saved you from sinking into the relentless quagmire of boredom!"

"Tell me the truth, Dottie. Does he sit in my chair during the day?"

"Mom! Marmaduke's in trouble again!"

"Okay, we watch that horror movie where the dogs take over the world!"

"Riding the school bus is no fun since Marmaduke comes along to keep an eye on us."

"Remember when he was a puppy and would snuggle down at our feet?"

"I've finished vacuuming."

"Have a hard day on the lawn?"

"How can you throw him out when he looks at you like that?"

"You mean, you're jealous of my DOLLY?"

"Marmaduke is bird watching the nest while the mother bird is getting worms!"

"I had no idea he liked broccoli!"

"I just finished my spring cleaning!"

"This happens every time I put on Beethoven's Fifth!"

"I thought this chair was getting kind of lumpy!"

"It's okay, Mom. They're Marmaduke's pets!"

"Why is it you have to be reassured every night that I still love you?"

"Want to lose weight? Walk past our house and we guarantee you'll lose at least five pounds!"

"You explain to him that he has to go home!"

"Enough target practice! Let's go swat some flies!"

"Marmaduke caught another dog catcher!"

"What do you mean, he's reading my mind?"

"You better find Marmaduke. I just heard that little boy say a big monster came out of the water and ate his hot dog!"

"He can leap into bed with us, but when he retires early, just TRY to leap into bed with HIM!"

"Marmaduke's up here ... strolling down Memory Lane!"

"You heard me, Marmaduke. Take it right back to that biology teacher's garage sale!"

"Who wants the first steak?"

"Someone has traded our picnic basket for one full of bones!"

"That's cat russian roulette!"

"You didn't eat your doggie vegetables again!"

"Who's next?"

"Good Heavens! Somebody's imported the Loch Ness Monster!"

"Next time Marmaduke is sick, let's keep it a secret!"

"I think he's planning to do some entertaining!"

"What makes you think you're any hotter than I am!"

"I suggest you apologize and make up with your family!"

"Burned dinner again!"

"Can Mr. Snyder come out and wrestle with Marmaduke?"

"I must say, this is truly conversation...First Marmaduke grunts then Phil groans!"

"Keep your paws off that horn!"

"And we can add robbery to those charges of disturbing the peace and resisting arrest!"

"C'mon, Marmaduke! Maybe the fish don't want to make friends with you!"

"LISTEN, ABSOLUTELY NO MORE DOG BISCUITS IN BED!"

"Have a bad dream?"

"GUESS WHO KNOCKED OVER THE TABLE WHEN THE KIDS WERE COLORING EASTER EGGS?"

"ON SECOND THOUGHT... JEFFY, GO FIRST!"

"Stop looking at me like that ... I am NOT giving up this chair!"

"Don't shake! Don't shake!"

"Okay, you! Visiting hours are over!

"I THINK IT'S SOMETHING CALLED 'SPRING FEVER'!"

"Marmaduke! Stop dunking your dog biscuits in my coffee!"

"Nonsense, Billy, you know that UFO's don't really exist!"

"It's no use! No matter how we throw it ... he always catches it!"

"I TRACED THE TUNNEL'S FULL LENGTH AND IT ENDS UP INSIDE CAVE'S MEAT MARKET!"

"MOM CLEANED OUT MARMADUKE'S DOGHOUSE AND THREW AWAY ALL HIS TOYS!"

"BUT, MOM! I WANTED TO STOP PLAYING BABY TWO HOURS AGO!"

"HOW COULD MARMADUKE HEAR US EATING MARSHMALLOWS WAY UP HERE?"

"Did you hear a loud 'slurp'?"

"No, thanks! This is one time I'll pass up my equal rights!"

"YOU DON'T LOOK LIKE A COFFEE TABLE TO ME! OFF!"

"I can't throw the stick for you right now! Please stop dropping it on my stomach!"

"You heard me ... DOWN!"

"AND IF YOU WALK WITH ME EVERY DAY, I'LL INTRODUCE YOU TO A COUPLE OF CUTE FRENCH POODLES!"

"Mom, will you make Marmaduke stop?"

"His water bed must have broken!"

"That was an excellent sales talk... but it didn't fool him a bit!"

"Aha! Thought I went out, didn't you!"

"...and another sales point is our lipsticks taste good!"

"I guess I better not ask if you caught anything!"

"... and please let Marmaduke make one touchdown so I can have my football back!"

"Car 17 needs help and requests back-up units..."

"Just think! All the other dogs will be jealous 'cause you'll be so warm!"

"Are you sure Phil asked you to help him?"

"I'M TIRED OF HAVING MY FACE LICKED!"

"STEADY, MOM! MARMADUKE LIKES TO SLEEP ON CLEAN SHEETS, TOO!"

"Uh, oh!"

"...CHASING A POLICE CAR AT 50 M.P.H. IN A 30 M.P.H. ZONE!"

"I dread making beds around here!"

"YOU HAD TO TAKE THEM TO SEE KING KONG!"

"Guess what, Mom. I taught Marmaduke how to roll over!"

I want to have a face-to-face talk about these empty candy bar wrappers!"

"I think we're being tailed!"

"Come out here and tell me what you've done!"

"Yeah, he's got all the can openers in there too!"

"As a matter of fact, we DON'T own a dog!"

"I DON'T RECALL THE VET SAYING ANYTHING ABOUT BREAKFAST IN BED!"

"YOU'LL EXCUSE ME IF I DON'T STAND UP FOR THE INTRODUCTION?"

"YES, I'M SURE SHE DIDN'T RIDE THE BUS HOME, TODAY!"

"His stomach talks in his sleep!"

"I know Marmaduke drank my chocolate milk! He has the straw in his mouth!"

"We lost 76-0. The other team had a girl dog!"

"It's another threatening letter from the country club."

"He sure makes himself comfy!"

"This is positively my last offer! Unlock the door and I'll give you THREE JUICY steaks!"

"Aww...Can't I lose my temper without you getting sore about it?"

"Talk about spoiled!"

"You didn't stay out very long!"

"Hey! Stop sampling Christmas!"

"Some Christmas present -- it's not even gift-wrapped!"

"At times like this, I realize it's all been worthwhile."

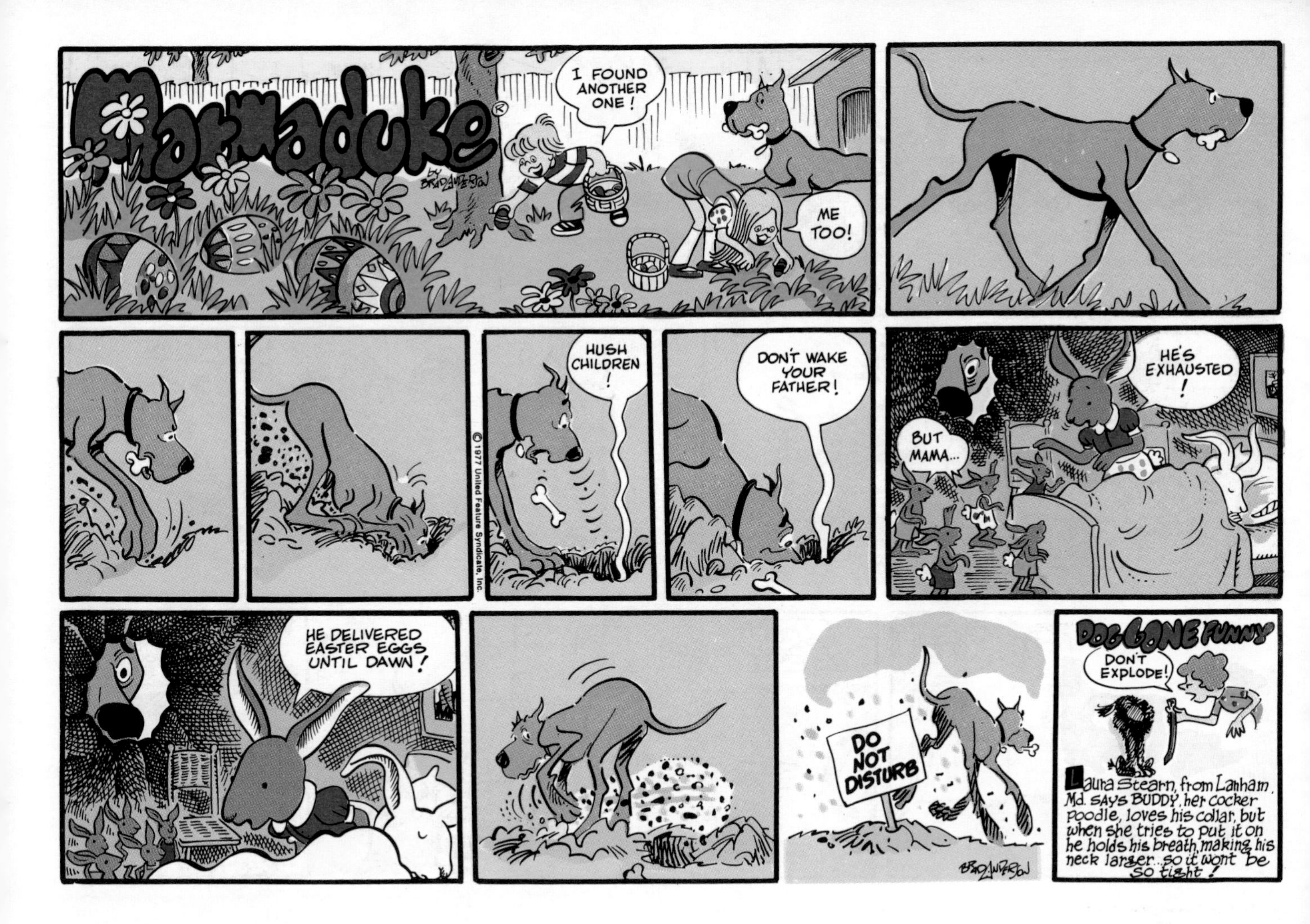
Marmaduke
I FOUND ANOTHER ONE!
ME TOO!
HUSH CHILDREN!
© 1977 United Feature Syndicate, Inc.
DON'T WAKE YOUR FATHER!
BUT MAMA...
HE'S EXHAUSTED!
HE DELIVERED EASTER EGGS UNTIL DAWN!
DO NOT DISTURB
BRAD ANDERSON
DOG GONE FUNNY
DON'T EXPLODE!
Laura Stearn, from Lanham, Md. says BUDDY, her cocker poodle, loves his collar, but when she tries to put it on he holds his breath, making his neck larger... so it won't be so tight!

CRUNCH
SMACK
RUF!
Tm. Reg. U.S. Pat. Off.—All rights reserved © 1976 by United Feature Syndicate, Inc.
WOOF!
WOOF
WOOF
BRAD ANDERSON
DOG GONE FUNNY
JACKIE LITTLE FROM NORTON SHORES, MICH., SAYS HER BIG BLACK AFGHAN MAKES THE SPARROWS VERY MAD WHEN SHE JUMPS UP IN THE BIRD BATH TO WASH HER FEET! NOW THAT'S FOR THE BIRDS!

Marmaduke®
by BRAD ANDERSON
YAWN
ZZZZZZ
© 1977 United Feature Syndicate, Inc.
GOOD BOY!
BRAD ANDERSON
DOG GONE FUNNY
HERE'S YOUR FAVORITE! FRUIT SALAD!
The 4 HENDRICK girls of FALLS CITY, ORE. tell us their part BOSTON TERRIER, BRISTOL LEE, eagerly awaits summer so he can enjoy the fresh fruit which he helps himself to by picking strawberries, blueberries, grapes, prunes, fallen apples and all the cherries he can reach!

DON'T MISS YOUR BUS!
BYE
OH, DEAR!!
PHIL FORGOT HIS HAT AND BRIEFCASE!
HERE, MARMADUKE!
CATCH PHIL!
HURRY! I HEAR THE BUS COMING!!
© 1978 United Feature Syndicate, Inc.
TRANSIT
I'VE SEEN EVERYTHING NOW!
BRAD ANDERSON
DOG GONE FUNNY
OH, NO! A TWO HOUR KOJAK SPECIAL
Mrs. Norma Landis lives in Dolton, Ill. Her OLD ENGLISH SHEEPDOG Patti Paws insists on sitting on Norma's lap and having her stomach rubbed while she watches police dramas on TV!

Marmaduke
by BRAD ANDERSON
RINGA-DING DINGA-DING DING
OH, MY GOODNESS!
RINGA DING DING
FIRST ICE CREAM TRUCK OF THE YEAR!
I TOLD HIM LAST YEAR!...
OH, NO
FREEZE ICE CREAM
RINGA DINGA DING
NO TRADES!!
FREEZE ICE CREAM
SO MUCH FOR YOUR NO TRADE POLICY!
BLUB
CHOKO FREEZE
DOG GONE FUNNY
My dog is a garbage disposal, says Mrs. LENA K. KIME from Biglerville, Pa. He eats all the ends when I snip green beans and he eats potato peelings.
© 1977 United Feature Syndicate, Inc.
BRAD ANDERSON

WE'RE GONNA CLEAN OUT YOUR DOGHOUSE!
IT'S REALLY A MESS!
NOW ISN'T THAT MUCH NICER?
DOG GONE FUNNY
WHERE HAVE YOU BEEN? I'VE BEEN WORRIED SICK!
Carolyn King of DOLTON, ILL. says her toy collie, Vicki, will pace the floor all night until her cat, MIDNIGHT, comes home. Then she cries with glee when MIDNIGHT comes in!
© 1977 United Feature Syndicate, Inc.
BRAD ANDERSON

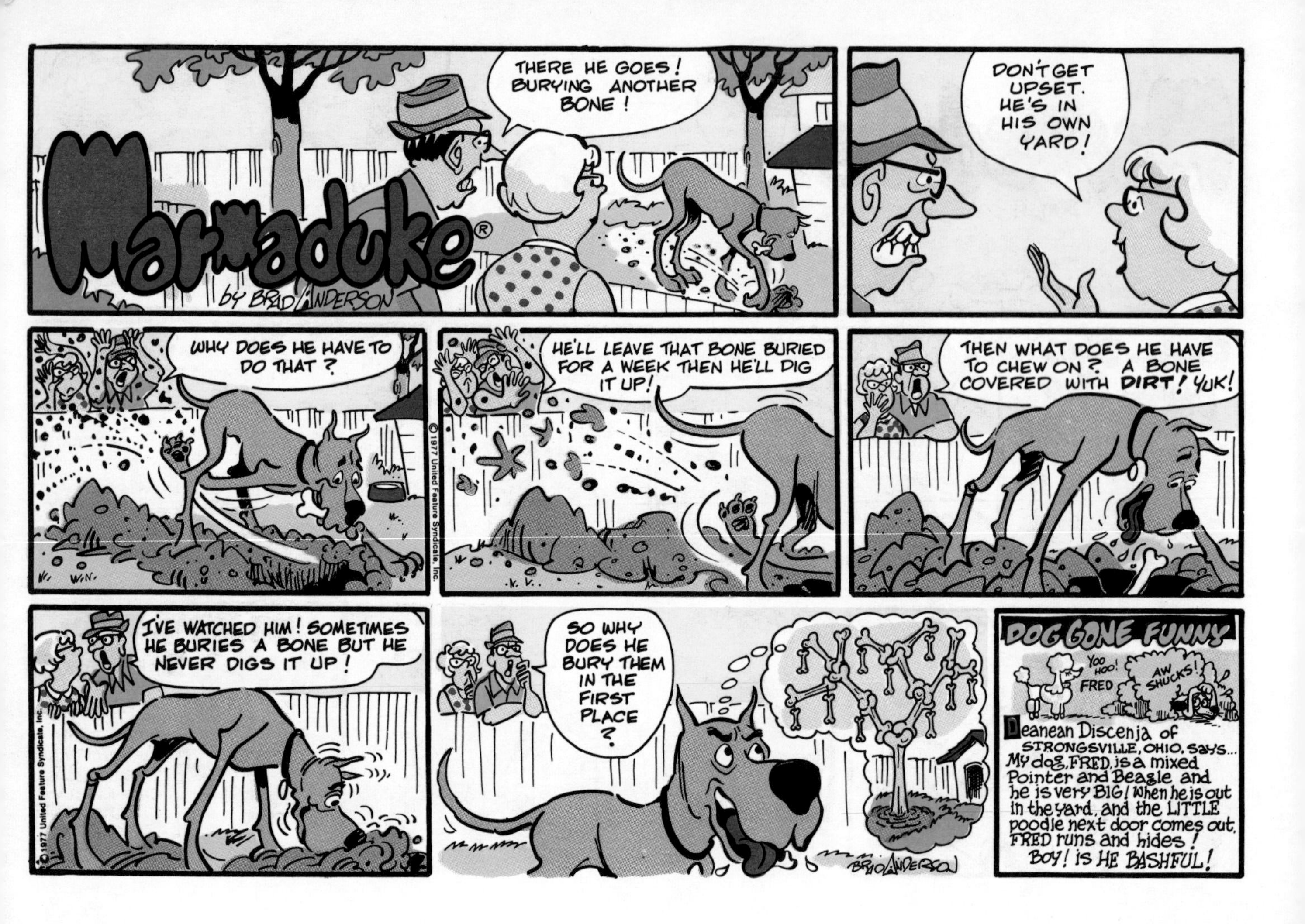
Marmaduke®
by BRAD ANDERSON
THERE HE GOES! BURYING ANOTHER BONE!
DON'T GET UPSET. HE'S IN HIS OWN YARD!
WHY DOES HE HAVE TO DO THAT?
HE'LL LEAVE THAT BONE BURIED FOR A WEEK THEN HE'LL DIG IT UP!
© 1977 United Feature Syndicate, Inc.
THEN WHAT DOES HE HAVE TO CHEW ON? A BONE COVERED WITH DIRT! YUK!
I'VE WATCHED HIM! SOMETIMES HE BURIES A BONE BUT HE NEVER DIGS IT UP!
© 1977 United Feature Syndicate, Inc.
SO WHY DOES HE BURY THEM IN THE FIRST PLACE?
BRAD ANDERSON
DOG GONE FUNNY
YOO HOO! FRED
AW SHUCKS!
Deanean Discenja of STRONGSVILLE, OHIO, says... My dog, FRED, is a mixed Pointer and Beagle and he is very BIG! When he is out in the yard, and the LITTLE poodle next door comes out, FRED runs and hides! Boy! is HE BASHFUL!

THIS IS MARMADUKE'S LIVING ROOM!
THIS IS HIS BONE COLLECTION
AND HERE'S MARMADUKE'S DINING ROOM! HE DOES A LOT OF ENTERTAINING!
© 1977 United Feature Syndicate, Inc.
HE LOVES HIS WATER MATTRESS!
WOW! THIS IS TOO MUCH! BUT WHAT'S REALLY AMAZING IS...
IT LOOKS SO MUCH SMALLER FROM THE OUTSIDE!
Marmaduke
BRAD ANDERSON
DOG GONE FUNNY
OH, NO!
Ann and David Roberts have a small black and white mixed breed named BOOTS. BOOTS likes to sleep anywhere except in her nice carpet-lined dog house! One morning they found her asleep in Mom's flower pot!! can you beat that?

Marmaduke
by Brad Anderson
WANT TO HEAR ME READ SOME NURSERY RYHMES?
NO
YES YOU DO!
NURSERY RYHMES
I'M NOT LISTENING TO YOU READ!
QUIET! YOU HAVE TO LISTEN!
OL' MOTHER HUBBARD WENT TO THE CUPBOARD...
AAGH!
TO GET HER POOR OL' DOG A BONE, AND WHEN SHE GOT THERE THE CUPBOARD WAS BARE...
© 1977 United Feature Syndicate, Inc.
AND SO THE POOR DOG HAD NONE!
SIGH
DOG GONE FUNNY
MOO
Renée Marsh's dog ZELA, in Columbia Station, Ohio, loves MILK! When she hears a cow moo on T-V, she races to the refrigerator and dances until she gets a glass of milk!

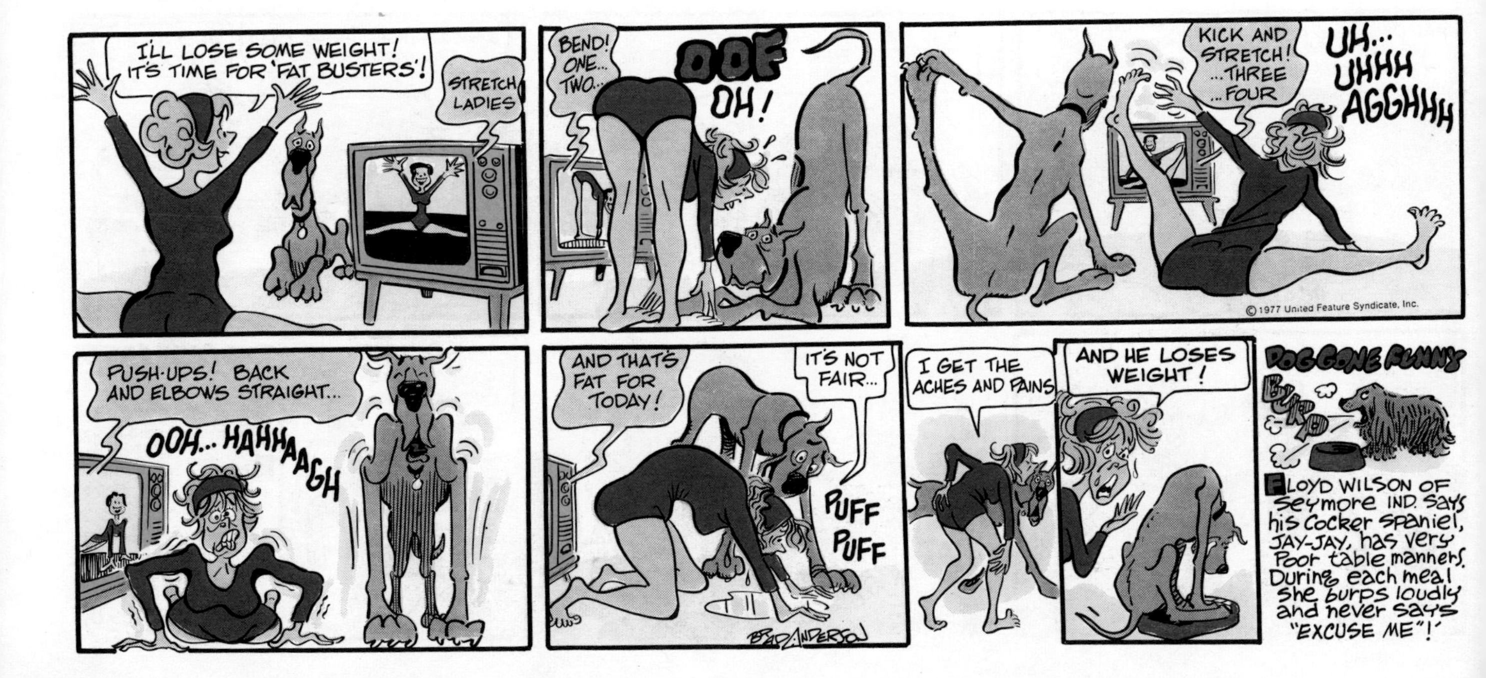

I'LL LOSE SOME WEIGHT! IT'S TIME FOR 'FAT BUSTERS'!
STRETCH LADIES
BEND! ONE... TWO...
OOF
OH!
KICK AND STRETCH! ...THREE ...FOUR
UH... UHHH AGGHHH
© 1977 United Feature Syndicate, Inc.
PUSH-UPS! BACK AND ELBOWS STRAIGHT...
OOH... HAHHAAGH
AND THAT'S FAT FOR TODAY!
IT'S NOT FAIR...
PUFF PUFF
I GET THE ACHES AND PAINS
AND HE LOSES WEIGHT!
DOG GONE FUNNY
FLOYD WILSON OF Seymore IND. Says his Cocker spaniel, JAY-JAY, has very Poor table manners. During each meal she burps loudly and never says "EXCUSE ME"!

Marmaduke
by BRAD ANDERSON
YAWN
MARMADUKE! GET OFF MY CLEAN BED!
© 1978 United Feature Syndicate, Inc.
I GAVE YOU A NICE RUG TO SLEEP ON!
THERE!
YOU SLEEP ON THAT!
BRAD ANDERSON
DOG GONE FUNNY
I'M COMING
WOOF
WOOF
WOOF
WOOF
Mrs George Lang lives in BREWSTER, N.Y., with SAM, a LAB-SHEPHERD MIX.
SAM patrols the rooms of the LANGS' house looking for SPIDERS on the ceiling. When he spots one, he sounds the alarm and the LANGS go into ACTION!

HALLOWEEN IS ONLY ONE WEEK FROM TOMORROW!
LETS MAKE A COSTUME FOR MARMADUKE!
© 1977 United Feature Syndicate, Inc.
HOW ABOUT USING THIS OLD FUR JACKET?
...AND MOM'S OLD WIG!
WE CAN USE THESE OLD PANTYHOSE!
AND THESE BOOTS!
GREAT! NOBODY WILL EVER GUESS WHO HE IS!
LET'S TAKE HIM OUT AND SEE!
BRAD ANDERSON
I DIDNT KNOW DOGS EVER GOT EMBARRASSED
MARMADU
DOG GONE FUNNY
TSK TSK KAREN FORGOT TO CLOSE HER DRAWER AGAIN
Karen Wisniewski of Maple Heights, Ohio, has a Peek-a-Poo, Charmy, who is very neat. If anyone leaves a drawer open, CHARMY gets up on her hind legs and pushes the drawer shut!

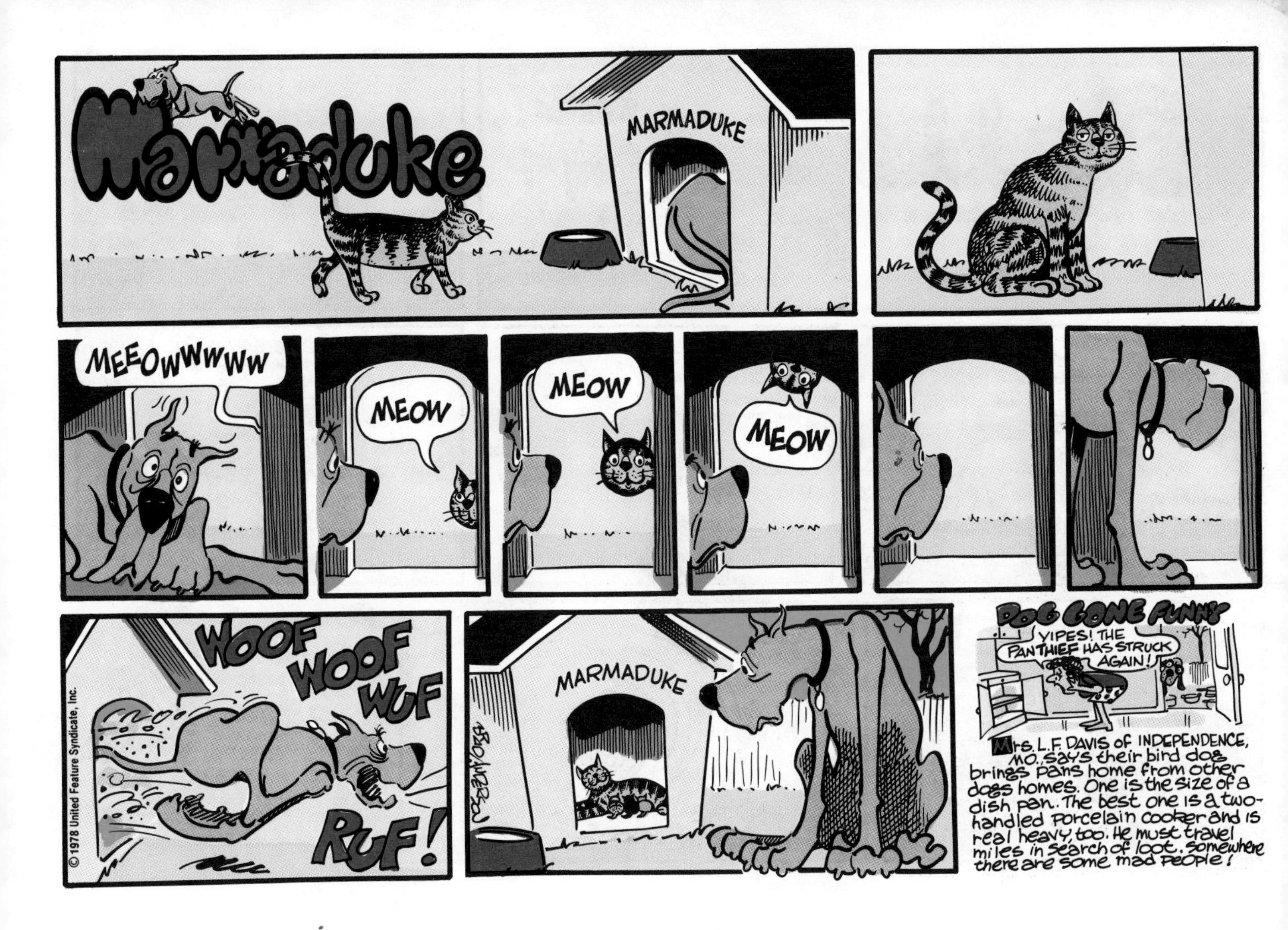
Marmaduke
MARMADUKE
MEEOWWWWW
MEOW
MEOW
MEOW
WOOF
WOOF
WUF
RUF!
© 1978 United Feature Syndicate, Inc.
MARMADUKE
BRAD ANDERSON
DOG GONE FUNNY
YIPES! THE PAN THIEF HAS STRUCK AGAIN!
Mrs. L.F. DAVIS of INDEPENDENCE, MO., says their bird dog brings pans home from other dogs homes. One is the size of a dish pan. The best one is a two-handled porcelain cooker and is real heavy, too. He must travel miles in search of loot. Somewhere there are some mad people!

HELP!
HELP!
© 1977 United Feature Syndicate, Inc.
WAA
YEA, MARMADUKE!
SIGH
WAAA
HELP
HELP
WE WANNA GET DOWN
HELP!
HELP!
HELP!
HELP!
BRAD ANDERSON
DOG GONE FUNNY
I THINK I'LL EAT A LIGHT SNACK
Ann Bereford of Dearborn, Mich., says her dog PEPPY chases flashlight light beams. He also tries to bite the rays of light!

Marmaduke
by BRAD ANDERSON
PHIL!
GO 'WAY!
PHIL... REMEMBER WHEN MARMADUKE BROUGHT HOME ALL THE NEIGHBORS' NEWSPAPERS?
UMPH
AND THE TIME YOU HAD TO RETURN ALL THOSE DOORMATS HE DRAGGED HOME?
UMN
AND THE TIME HE STOLE ALL THE PANS AT THE CHURCH PICNIC AND...
MMN?
© 1978 United Feature Syndicate, Inc.
WELL THE CURATOR AT THE MUSEUM JUST CALLED...
AND WE'RE IN TROUBLE!
DOG GONE FUNNY
ACHOO
Jimmy White from STACY, Minnesota, tells us that he has a doberman pinscher named REGGIE. Whenever anyone sneezes, REGGIE sneezes, too!
ACHOO

OOH, LA! LA! DOGGIE MUNCHIES! ZEY ARE DIVINE, DAHLING!
DOGGIE MUNCHIES
I LIKE THE WAY THEY CRUNCH! IT'S A REAL DOG'S DOG FOOD!
DOGGIE MUNCHIES
RIDICULOUS COMMERCIAL! EVERYONE KNOWS DOGS CAN'T TALK!
OH, YEH! THAT'S JUST YOUR OPINION, BUSTER!
DOTTIE, YOU'RE NOT GOING TO BELIEVE THIS, BUT...
HOW TO THROW YOUR VOICE
BRAD ANDERSON © 1977 United Feature Syndicate, Inc.
DOG GONE FUNNY
ZZZZZ
Miss Ponder Lee Brown of Cleburne, Tex. has a four-pound Chihuahua, COUNTESS. In order to get into PONDER'S chair, COUNTESS ① climbs a ladder leaning against the bed, ② jumps down onto the bed, ③ runs to the edge of the bed, ④ leaps to the chair... and takes a nap!